The BIG BIG BOOK of MAZES

The
BIG
BIG
BOOK
of
MAZES

Nathan Locke & Matthew Locke

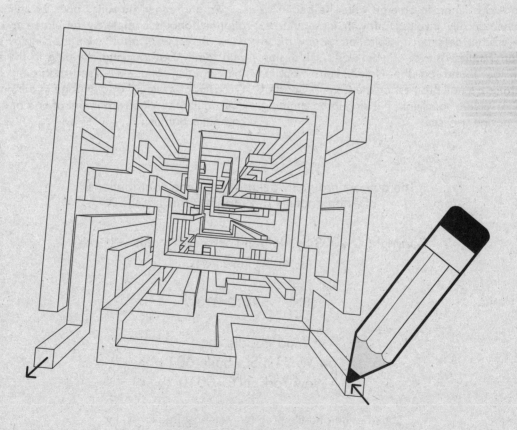

MUD PUDDLE, INC.
New York, New York

To family, whose faith makes us what we can become.

About the Authors

The two major talents behind the mazes in this book are brothers Nathan Locke and Matthew Locke. They have self-dubbed themselves MazeMasters. Though Nathan is the elder, both brothers started drawing mazes as small children. They have each refined their maze-authoring skills through years of practice, lots of encouragement from family and friends, and not a small bit of friendly competition.

Nathan initially began drawing mazes as an idle distraction, the results of which could be shown to his father for a willing smile. Nathan has always set out to master any new maze styles he encounters and must thank several friends for their unknowing contribution to this work. Over the years, a new twist on a perfectionist's obsession to excel began to emerge when he began to mix his mathematically inspired art with these mazes. Presently, he actually gets much inspiration for new maze constructs from Matthew's ever-original works. His design artwork can be found on the Nate73.com website. Nathan operates a small business on the Central Coast of California that caters to clients needing programming and website design services.

Matthew may have started out looking up to Nathan and learning to imitate his maze styles, but has clearly long since outstripped him the arena of pioneering creative new maze styles as demonstrated in many of the sections in this book. While Matthew is generally quite modest, Nathan will boast on his behalf that he has a truly rare ability to creatively develop completely unique maze styles, especially dimensional illusions. Matthew also has an uncommon knack for JavaScript and many visitors to MegaMazes.com have enjoyed his iMazor maze game. Matthew works in Northern California as a windows and web programmer for a midsize IT corporation.

Among other pursuits, both brothers enjoy recreational hobbies completely unrelated to mazes or artwork. By order of priority, we most enjoy spending time with family, backpacking/climbing in the High Sierra in the summer, and skiing/snowboarding in the winter. Occasionally, we will also engage in a friendly all-nighter duel within the VR environment of one of our favorite 3D computer games.

The authors gratefully acknowledge the contributions
of Arion Phoenix in preparing this book.

ISBN: 1-59412-010-2

Mud Puddle Inc.
54 W. 21st St., Suite 601
New York, NY 10010

Book design and file prep by Mulberry Tree Press, Inc.
www.mulberrytreepress.com

CONTENTS

CHAPTER 1 • Great Grids

CHAPTER 2 • Design Warps

CHAPTER 3 • Patterns: Organized Chaos

CHAPTER 4 • Over and Unders

CHAPTER 5 • Freehand

CHAPTER 6 • 3-D Illusions

CHAPTER 7 • MegaMaze Miscellany

CHAPTER 8 • Modifications: Altered States

SOLUTIONS

INTRODUCTION

Welcome to *The Big Big Book of Mazes*, a collection of mazes from the MegaMazes.com website! The website boasts an incredibly extensive array of the most high-quality printable mazes available anywhere on the Internet. We have selected the finest and most innovative works created for the website and assembled them all into one book. We are proud to present to you many completely original maze styles that are at once uniquely unconventional and quintessentially elegant. While you will also find a wide variety of traditional mazes, you will discover our distinctive artistic flair to be a refreshing break from the ordinary.

• • •

As MegaMazes.com is the originating Internet website for the mazes in this book, it may interest you to learn how the site came about. After a gradual accumulation of compliments from family and friends, primary authors and brothers Nathan and Matthew each came to believe that others would really like a chance to take on their maze challenges. By all means, please do prove us right and buy this book!

Having both created dozens of websites, and given the potential for worldwide exposure on the Internet, the choice for the brothers to use the web as a venue was obvious. A plan was made and specific goals were set to try and create the biggest, most fun, and coolest kid-appropriate and content-rich website ever dedicated to mazes. The intent was to utilize their specialized programming knowledge in order to reach the entire world with their mazes.

New challenges arose since, while having considered themselves as MazeMasters for some time, the authors had not yet utilized their convoluted skills with any media other than ink pen on paper. Due to the many restrictions and particulars of efficiently and securely publishing artwork to the web, it became apparent that an alternate authoring method was going to be necessary. After some research, it was decided that scalable vector graphics would be created and then packaged into a specialized but common format known as PDF. So, though the authors had long ago refined their skills at drawing mazes and built up a large portfolio, it was not actually until only recently that the majority of the mazes on the website, and those in this book, were created.

It truly became persistence and old-fashioned hard work, though, which got the job done. Production of this whole new crop of mazes for the website hasn't stopped once the task was first undertaken. As a subscription selling point, new mazes are released each week.

• • •

There are certain key techniques that are used by the self-accredited MazeMasters when engaged in the practice of authoring their mazes. It may be useful for would-be solvers of the mazes in this book to understand the type and levels of thinking that go into every maze contained herein. Knowing the authors and their amazing concepts may aid in an easier discovery of solutions.

A discussion concerning the mazes in this book must begin by defining a term that has been coined by the MegaMazes' founders: MAZERY. As defined on the website, mazery is: ". . . the sundry mystical and arcane powers of the mind utilized when creating a maze. Mazery involves the use of all manner of optical, mathematical, and psychological trickery in order to maximize the confusion of pathways in a maze." In a more general sense, this term is used to collectively describe the effective use of specific methods employed during the authorship of mazes, but also implies a certain amount of sadism with regards to the creator's obsessive intent to generate a maximum effect of disorientation and minimize solvability of a maze.

You see, every attempt is made to fully achieve a particular type of subterfuge in each maze. Specific maze styles seem to lend themselves more easily to certain ploys than other styles do. For example, a hex grid style maze can often be made more difficult through the use of many short and twisting passage segments with many dead-end offshoots, but hex grids are not generally effective at helping to mask the solution when long stretches of parallel passages are used. For a maze author, an intimate knowledge of a chosen style is paramount when determining the best way to make a maze.

During the development of a maze, every effort must be made by the designer to predict the thought-process of someone attempting to solve the puzzle. If, for example, it appears as if part of a maze solution should logically flow down a certain pathway, this will be used against the reader. Indeed, every effort will be made to encourage this illusion; the correct solution branch will be made to appear as unassuming as possible. Readers beware, though, for the game has barely begun and will go way beyond this point. At the next few subsequent junctures, this stratagem may be expected. Therefore, a new tact may be utilized. Or not. It just depends on the maze and the intent of the author. Sometimes the best policy is to repetitively use special chicanery so many times in a row that a reader keeps trying the obvious solutions for naught; i.e., thinking that sooner or later the right answer has to be, say, turn right when it has been left the last dozen or more times. In fact, enforcing the proverbial Murphy's Law in a maze effectively ensures its success. The judicious use of reverse psychology as well as the occasional use of double- and triple-reverse psychologies has an indisputable track record.

The issue at hand is that while pure randomness in a maze does present a challenge to solve, there are certain countering methods or algorithms that a reader might apply for the purpose of determining the solution in a faster than average time. All of the mazes hand-created by true MazeMasters do not principally resort to a mere uncreative but massive proliferation of passageways to achieve a chaotic melee. The mazes in this book were carefully and individually crafted to lure the reader down the wrong path at every turn. Sure, on occasion, simple luck can prevail. Eventually, it may be that a reader outsmarts a certain area of a maze. Before getting complacent, though, know many other traps will waylay the rest of the solution. And be assured that we will do our best to match wit for wit and continue to make every successive maze a distinctly difficult obstacle. The longer it takes you solve a maze, the more skilled we can assume its author to be. In the end, every maze created should be as confusing as possible—the more difficult the maze, the more thrilling the journey. And the mazes created in this fashion are, thereby, quite a lot of fun.

Truly, for the enthusiast, a maze that does not present a masterful sense of trickery is not a maze at all but merely a scripted, uninteresting jaunt. As a reader of this book, you are looking for more than the average maze. You are seeking all of the classic elements of sheer adventure. First there is a difficult challenge. Then there is the requirement of endurance, of intellectual dexterity, and persistence. Traversing the maze becomes an expedition. Finally, once a proper level of determination is applied, and if the solution inevitably unravels for you, there is a vastly rewarding sense of accomplishment—victory!

• • •

Of course, the goals of MegaMazes.com and our concept of mazery may be lofty—so only you can truly judge their success. See our ad in the back for more information on the website, but once you are through with this book do come for a visit. You can use the feedback area to let the MazeMasters know what you think of the site and this book.

All of the maze art amassed into this book was initially created for the website, but done so with the idea in mind that a publisher might someday find our work marketable. Once we brought the website online in January of 2003, we didn't have to wait long. Interest was expressed in publishing our mazes a mere few months afterwards. Our thanks go out to Mud Puddle Books for all of their work in publishing and promoting this book.

Chapter 1

GREAT GRIDS

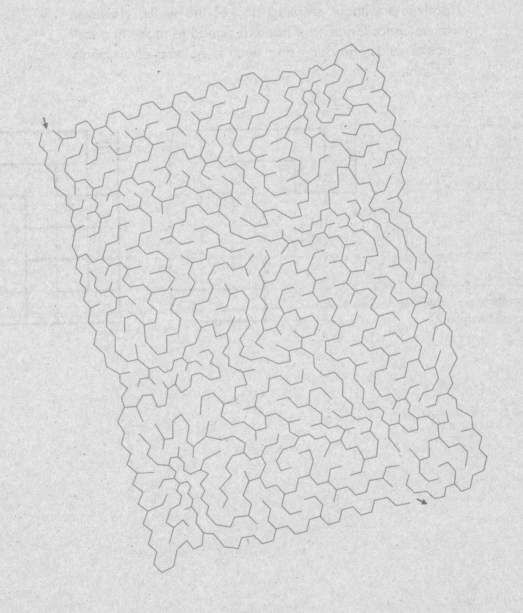

Chapter 1 • Introduction

Perhaps the most well-known and intuitive form of a maze, grid style mazes present a set of walls creating passages in certain regularly repeating increments. Square and hexagonal grids provide the most common basis mesh for this type of maze. To solve grid mazes, one must merely proceed from start to finish along the pathways without crossing any of the walls. However, these Great Grids have been designed to make that task easier said than done and each is quite a diversionary delight.

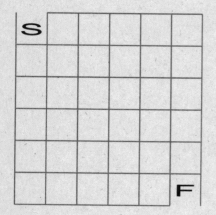 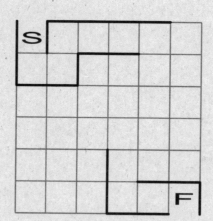 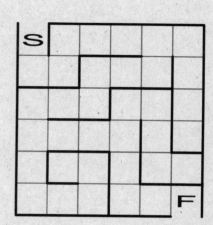

SimpleGrid

start

finish

Solution page 144

Classic Grid

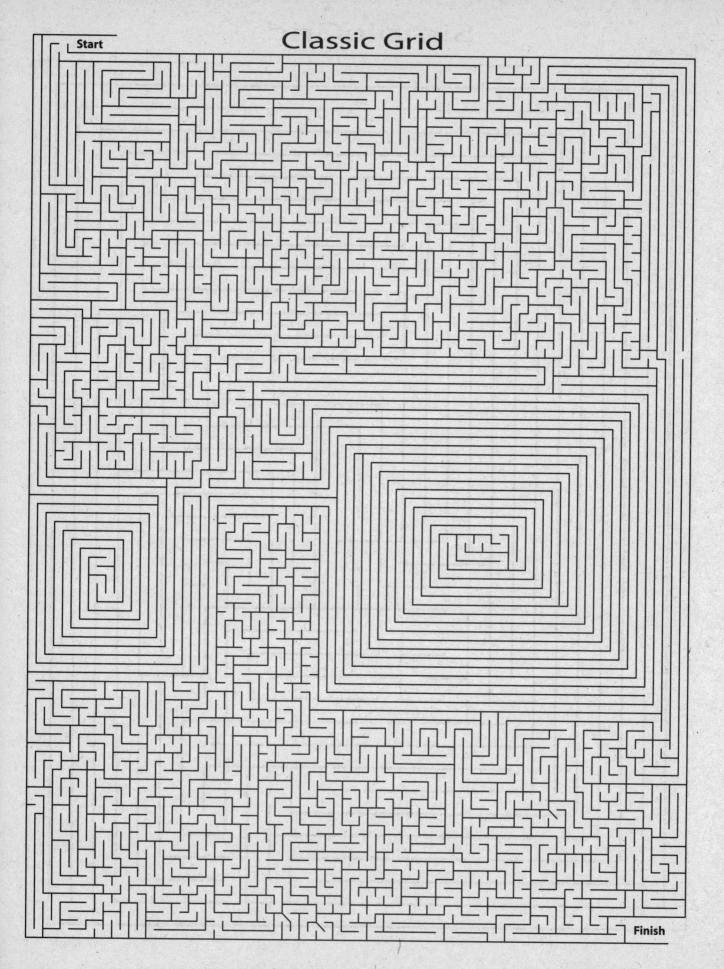

Finish

14

Solution page 147

HEXMAZE

Start

Finish

HEXXED

Solution page 148

HexHills

Hex Vortex

Solution page 149

BubbleHex

HEXHATCH

Solution page 150

Hexillusion

Solution page 152

Tunnel In - Tunnel Out

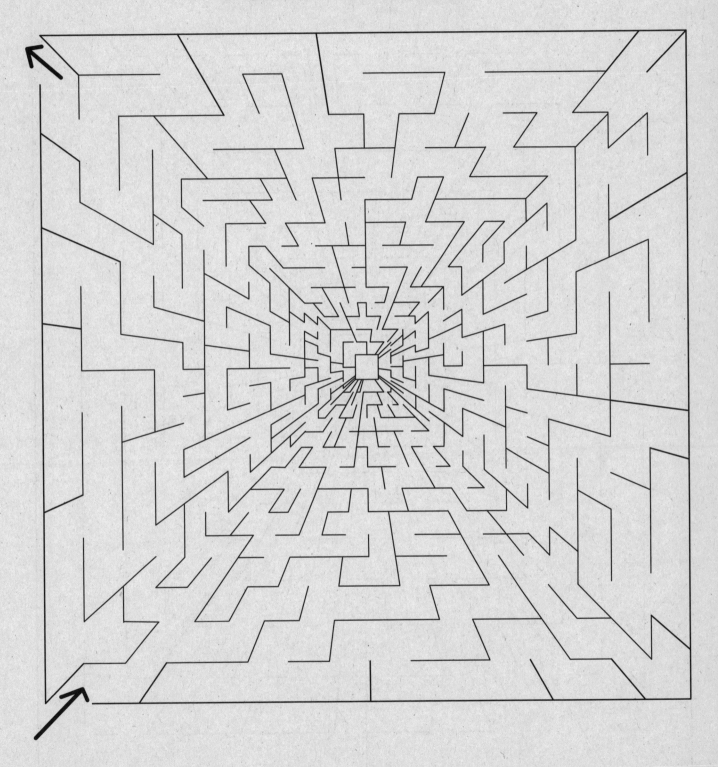

Solution page 153

PerspectiveWallz

SquareWarp

Solution page 154

FourFall

Start

Finish

CubesGrid

Solution page 155

Dimensional Grid

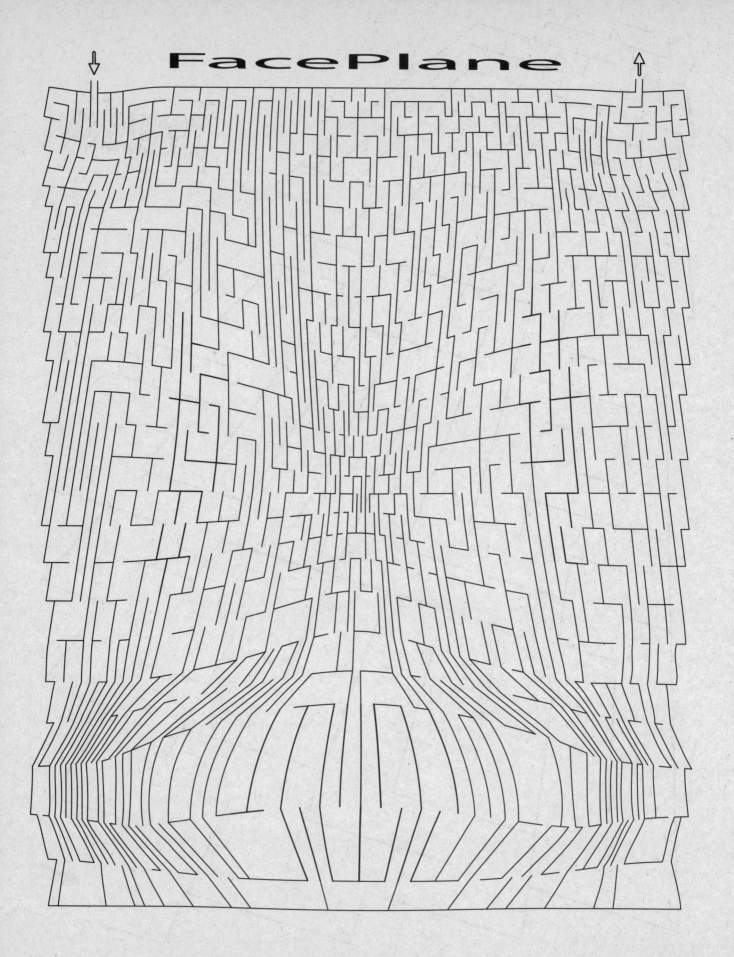

Solution page 156

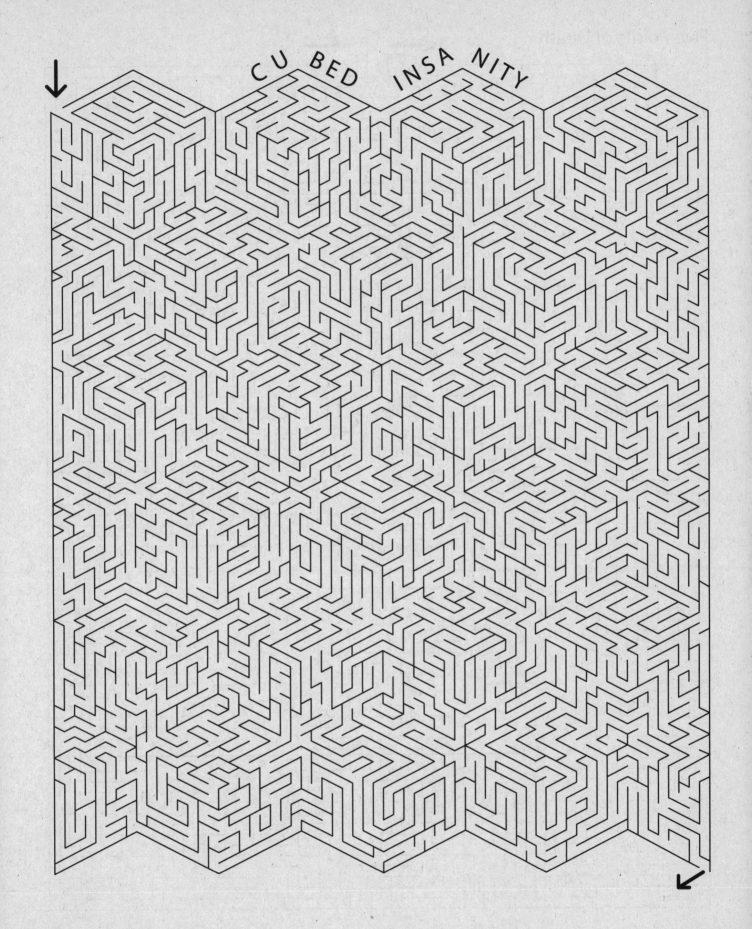

CU BED INSA NITY

Five Points of Death

Solution page 157

ELLIPTIMAZING

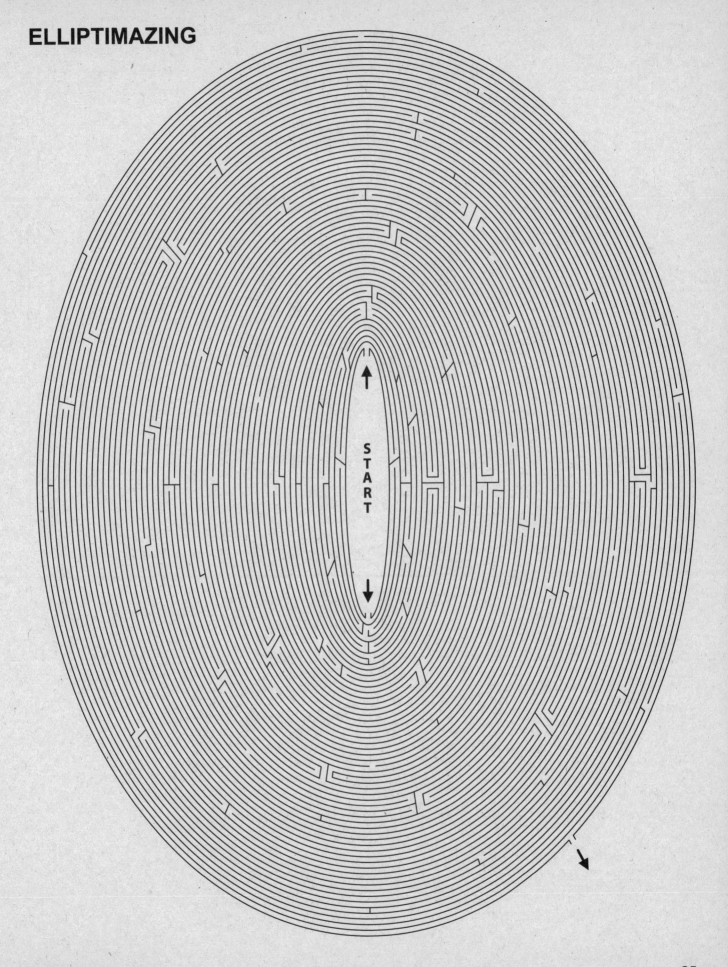

START

Chapter 2
DESIGN WARPS

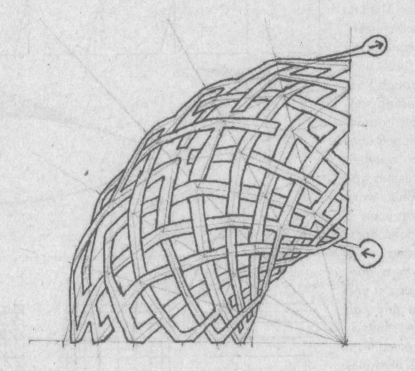

Chapter 2 • Introduction

The designer styles of our mazes are perhaps the most accomplished trademark of the MegaMazes.com website. These mazes are based upon a wide range of spectacular design warps. The mazes are essentially similar in structure to square grid mazes, but are created using warp schemes. These designs are based upon simple linear concepts that are warped into particular configurations that are intended to offer a very convincing 3-dimensional illusion.

Our design mazes are inspired by the neo-modern Op Art created under the pseudonym "Nate73" by co-author Nathan Locke. While the colorized modifications of these line mazes are regarded as especially impressive artwork, much of his self-proclaimed "polychromatic optical illusory art" is actually based on relationships of filled shapes. Take a look at Nate73.com for more information on this art style, image samples, and art available for purchase.

There are two basic types of warp schemes used to create the maze art in this chapter. The first scheme is based upon the essentially 1-dimentional concept of incrementally shifting both ends of a line segment through itself and a second, intersecting segment at steady intervals in order to form a series of clipped lines that approach one another. Figure 2-1 demonstrates this type of warp. The second warp scheme seen is based upon a more fully 2-dimensional concept of using two criss-crossing sets of lines in order to form a grid. Often, drawing diagonals and removing the original grid can significantly enhance the 3-dimensional illusion created from this effect. Figure 2-2 illustrates an example of this technique.

With one exception, the mazes in this chapter are solved the same as regular grid mazes in that you are not allowed to cross through walls. However, the last maze in this chapter is an over-under maze and for that maze pathway travel can cross under another path when extending through the other side.

Figure 2-1

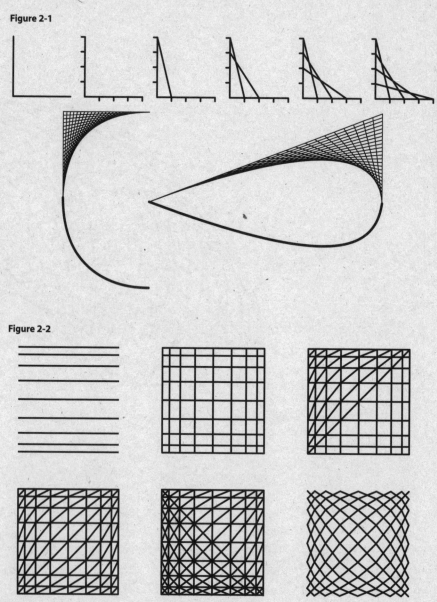

Figure 2-2

LineZoid

Elliptoroid Grid

Finish

Hexa**Bulge**

WarpDrains

wormhole

ShutterWarp

Solution page 163

Snakey

Peanut

Solution page 164

HexaFlower

TRITOR INTERLEAVE

Solution page 166

Circumplex

Wormhole II

Solution page 168

Peanut II

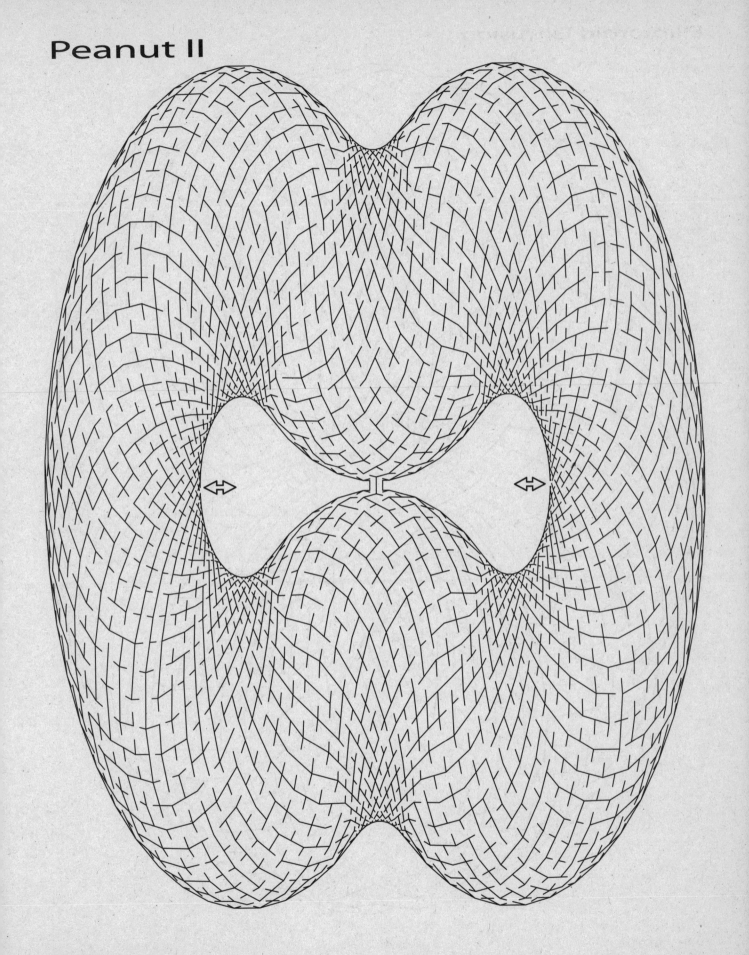

Elliptoroid Extrusion

Solution page 168

Chapter 3

PATTERNS

ORGANIZED CHAOS

Chapter 3 • Introduction

Sometimes, despite all of the wonderfully perplexing aspects and functional precision of regular grid mazes, it takes an unorthodox, interesting pattern in order to accomplish the creation of a truly original maze. In this chapter, we present to you mazes that have a seemingly chaotic array of lines that, in fact, are part of a larger pattern. Solutions that evade the eye are the deliberate effect of this bit of magical patchwork.

Rules for these mazes are the same for regular grid mazes in that you cannot cross through walls and must remain within the passages from Start to Finish.

Figure 3-1 | **How pattern mazes are created.**

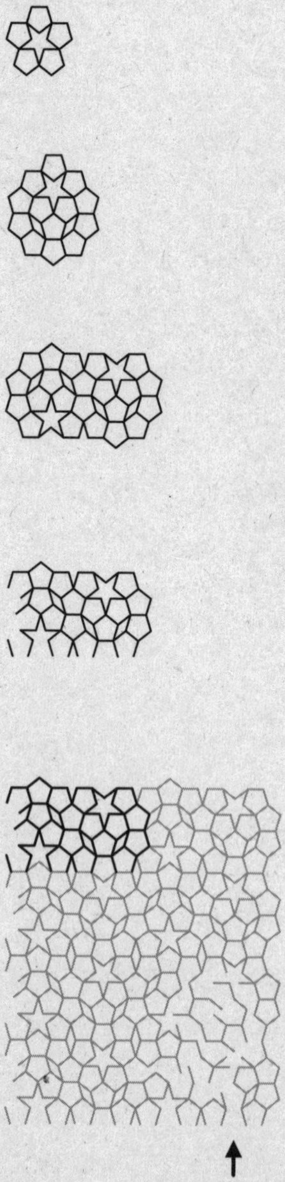

It is first necessary to start with a simple formation.

Next comes experimention that adds onto the basic idea.

Effect a natural repetition in the pattern.

The most challenging part is usually to extract out just the repeating element. This will be just the vital piece that, when joined onto itself, actually creates the pattern.

Finally, a large pattern mesh is built from which an original pattern maze can be created.

GRIDLOCK

Solution page 170

HEXISTIC

Downpour

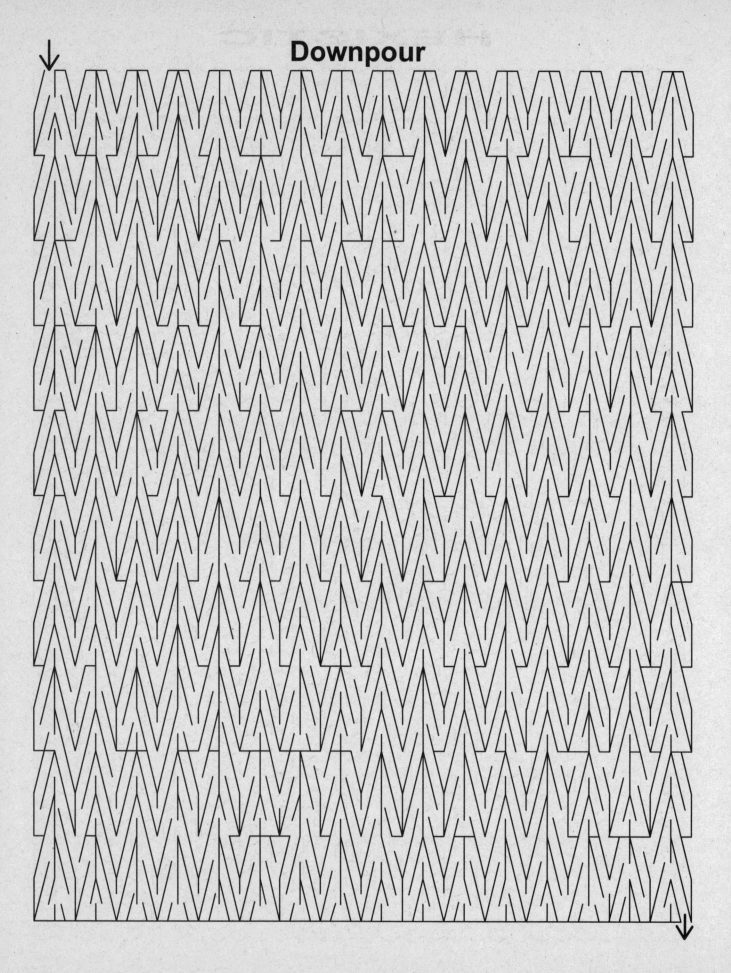

Solution page 172

Descention

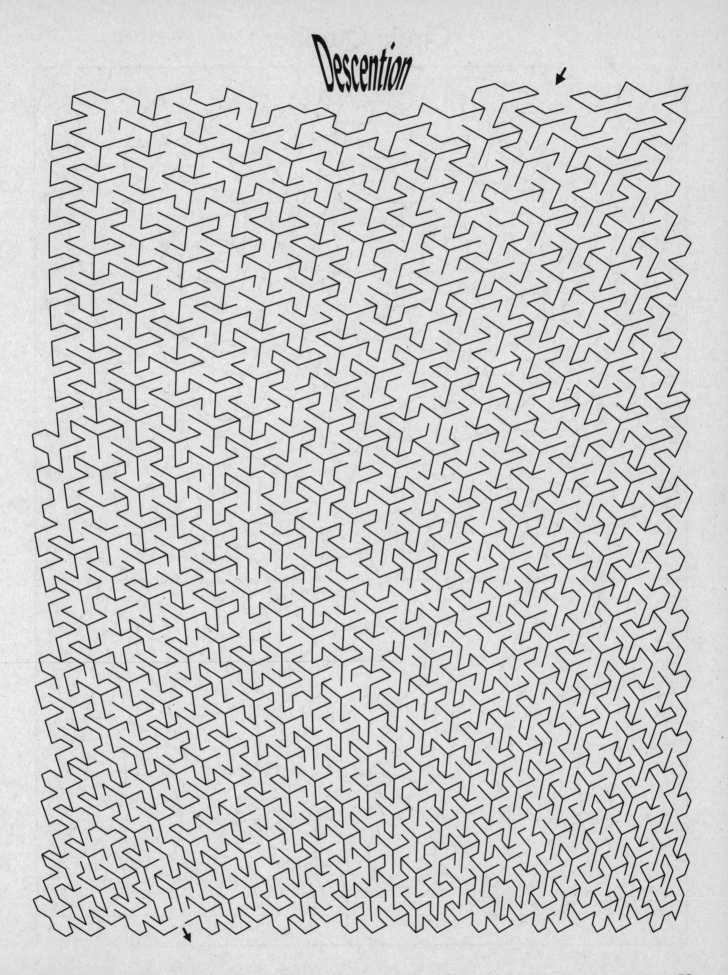

Solution page 172

Circle Quirkle

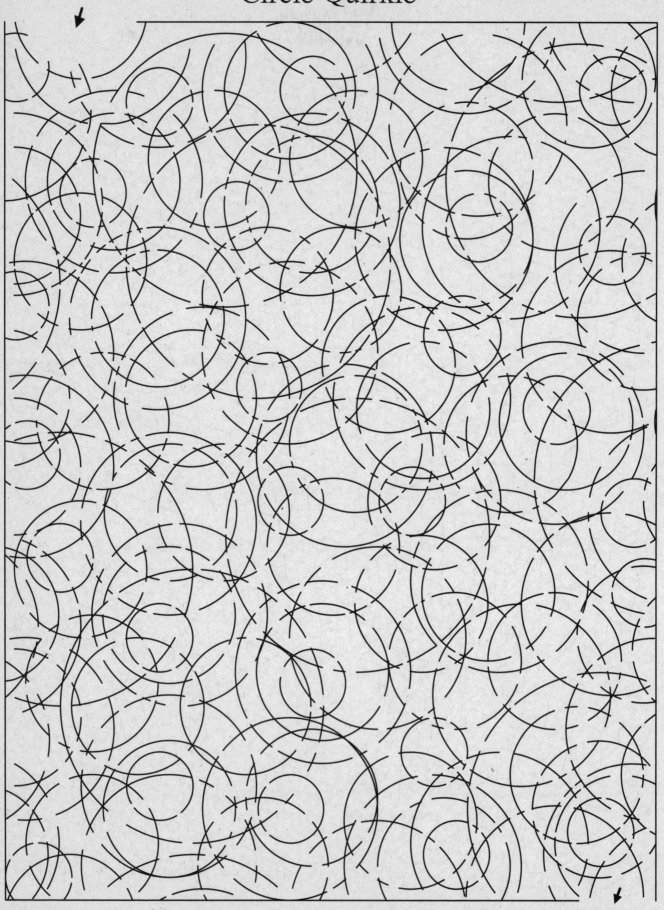

Solution page 174

PentaStarz

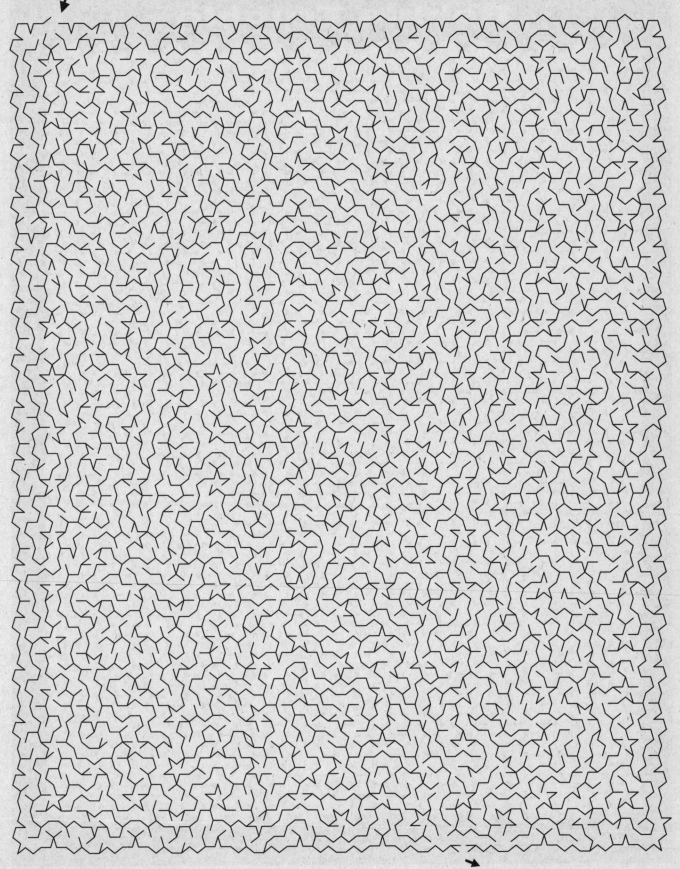

Bubble Trubble

start

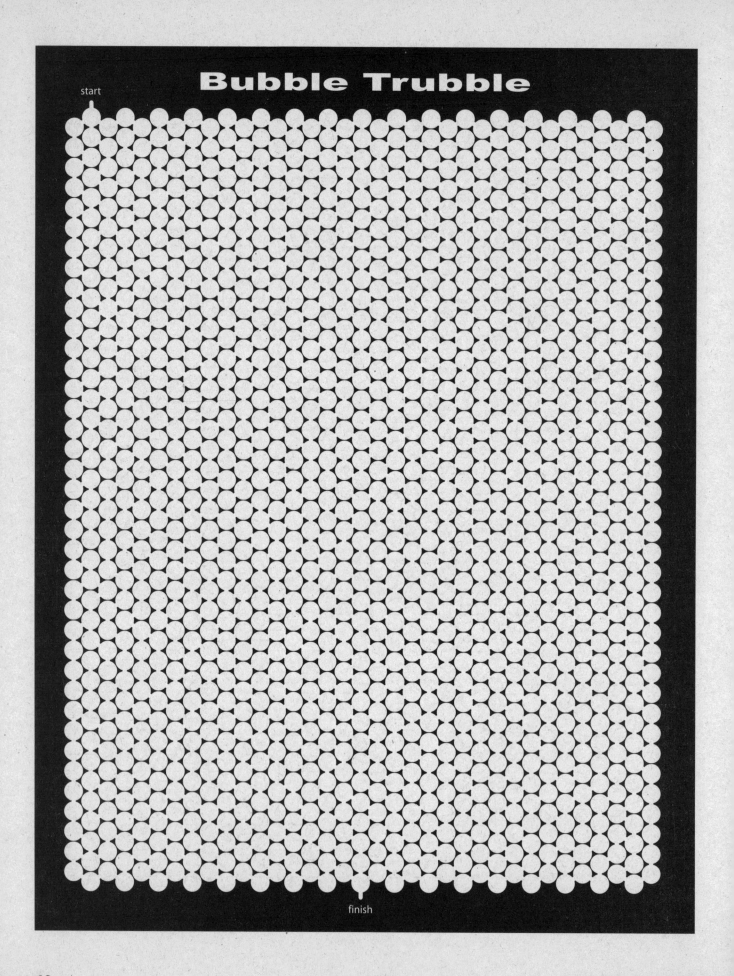

finish

Solution page 174

SnakesEyes

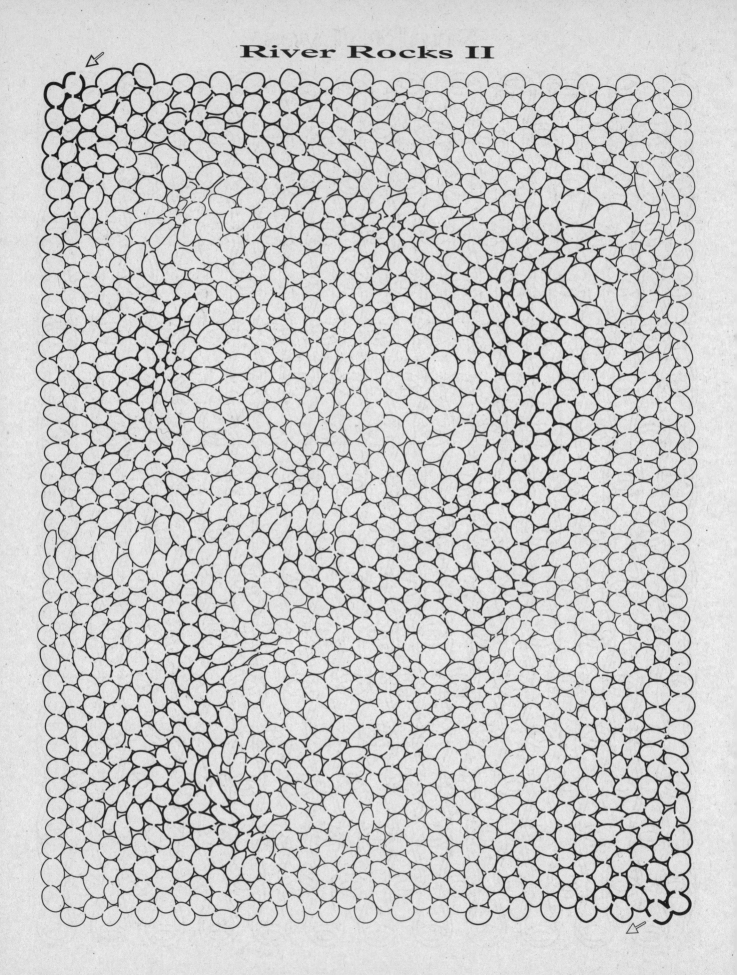

Solution page 176

Circle Starz

Solution page 175

Chapter 4

OVERS
AND
UNDERS

Chapter 4 • Introduction

While grid and other mazes with two-dimensional solutions are quite intuitive, it is certain that you will find our over-and-under mazes to be a whole new challenge. Though in many structural ways similar to the pattern mazes presented in Chapter 3, we now introduce a new level of difficulty – the ability to cross under a path and emerge on the opposite side.

At first glance, these 3-D pattern mazes appear to be a continuously repeating pattern. In actuality, though, any pattern is 'broken' in certain places, creating the branching passages of the maze. The very nature of these mazes tends to distract the eye and their circular, tangled nature causes them to be very confusing mazes.

To solve an over-and-under maze, any passage can be followed through the other side of one that it intersects. Note that passages can only go underneath another pathway for the width of the upper pathway. If no other "side" of the passage is visible or possible within that width, then that passage is a dead-end.

Woven Lies

Start

End

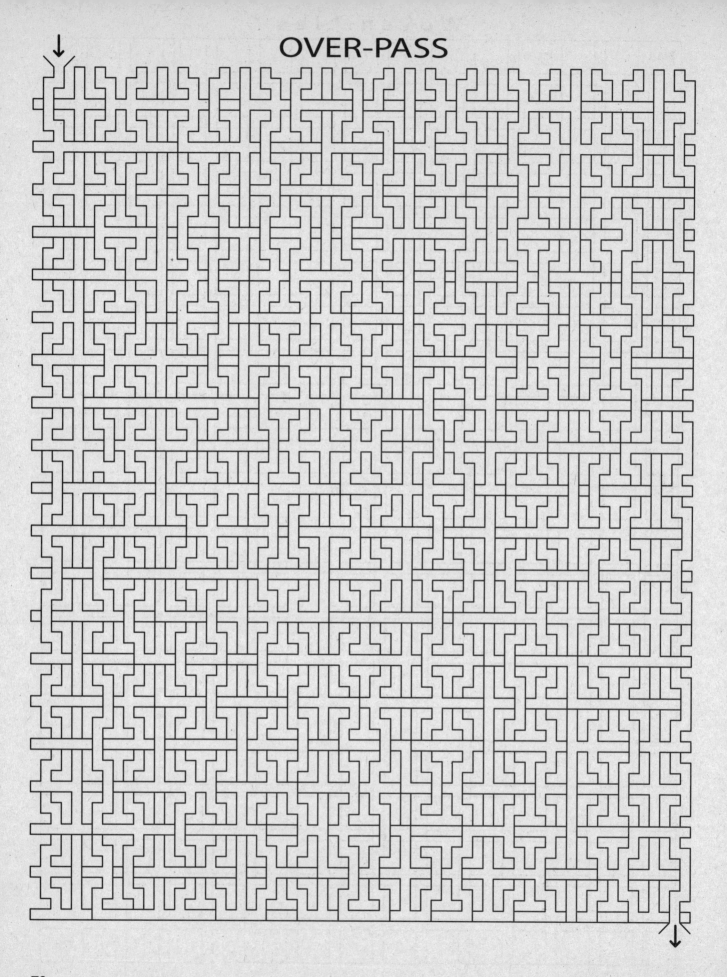

Solution page 178

Mesh-Mess

START

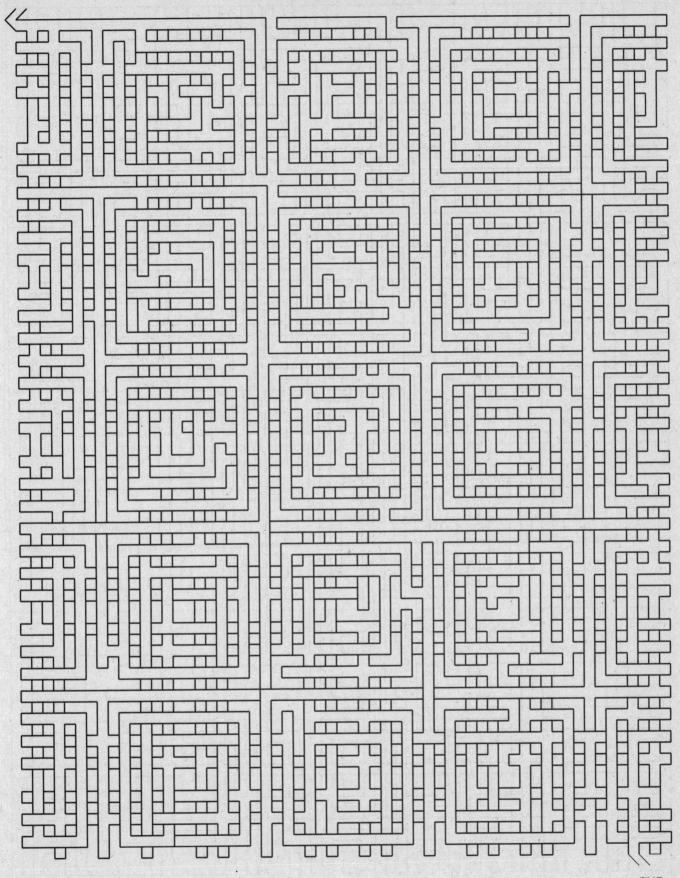

END

PATHWAY TO.... ?

Start

End

Solution page 179

Woven Boxes

Shape Down

Solution page 181

STIX

Ring Connectrix

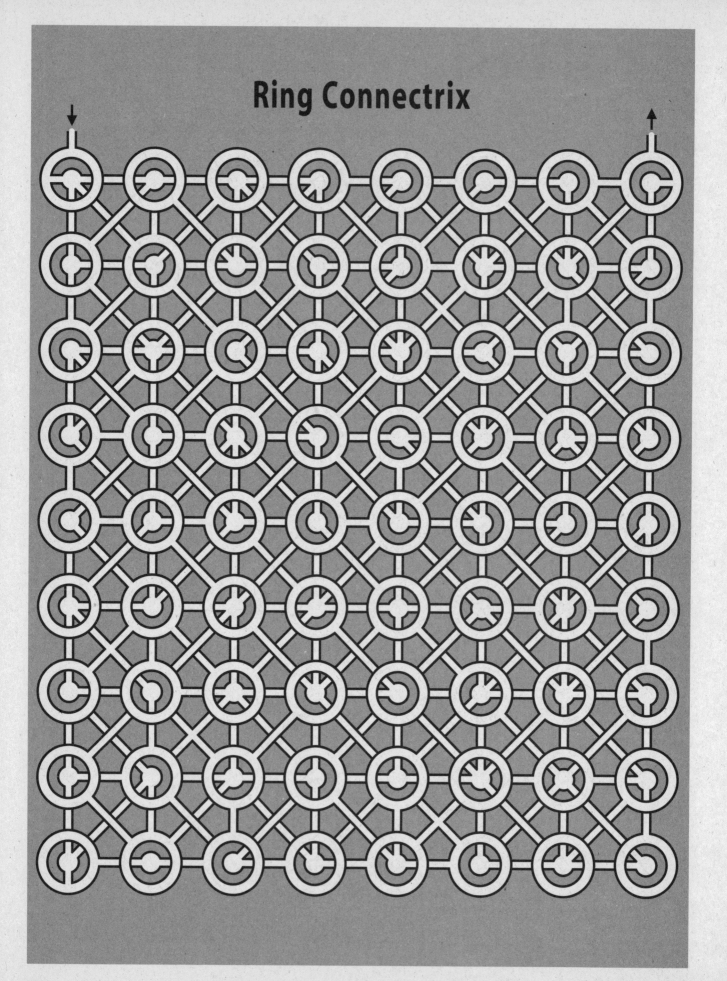

Solution page 182

Connecentrix

Chapter 5

FREEHAND

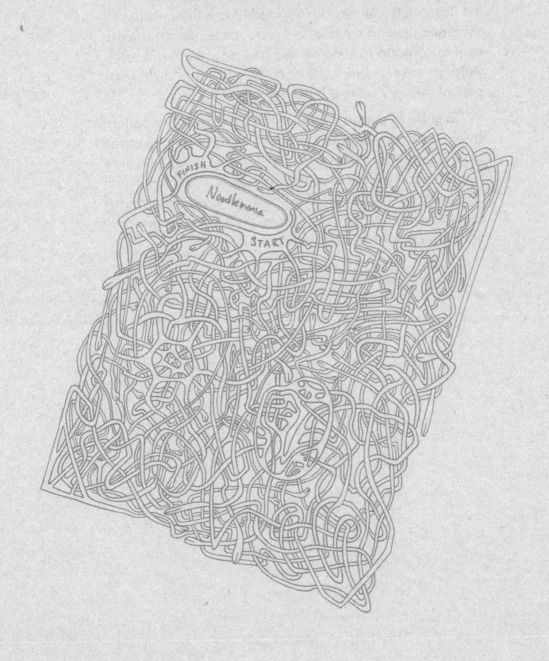

Chapter 5 • Introduction

In this chapter, we present many of the early original, hand-drawn artwork that led to the eventual creation of the MegaMazes.com website. First there are the freestyle twisting and turning passages of the "brain" style mazes. Next, there are the interwoven, tortuous complexities of the "spaghetti" mazes. Also included are the deceptively simplistic looking squared freestyle mazes which appear as if to conform to a demented grid or pattern but rarely yield an easy or quick solution. Finally, there are examples of the very unique jumping mazes.

To solve freehand mazes of the brain, grid, or pattern styles, your chosen path cannot cross through any of the walls that form the maze. Solving the spaghetti-style mazes require that travel may proceed under one path and back out the other side. Solving the jumping mazes requires travel from box to box of the maze but only along the arrows in their indicated direction.

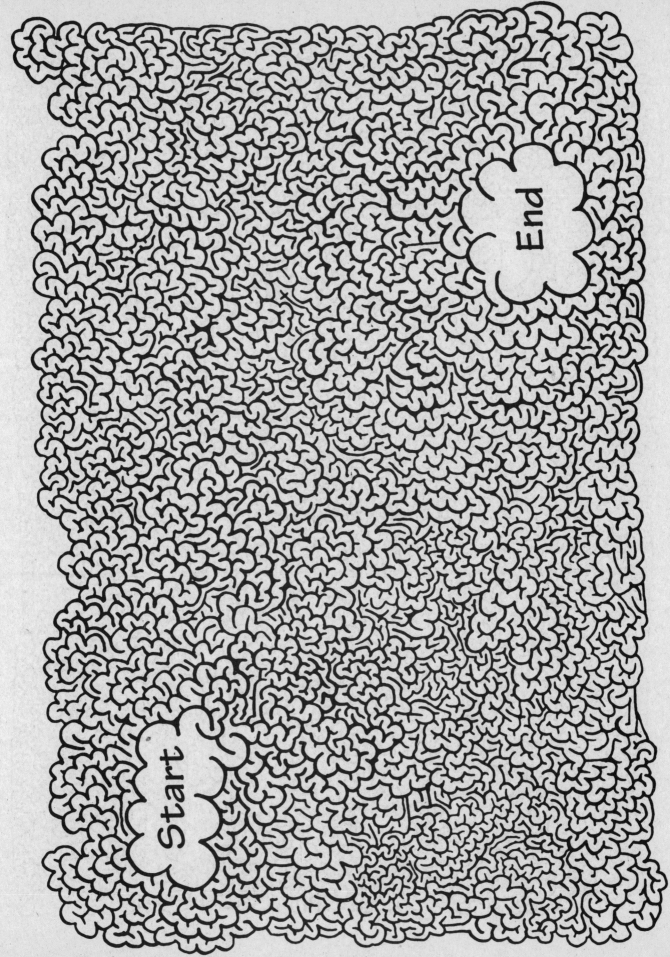

82

Solution page 185

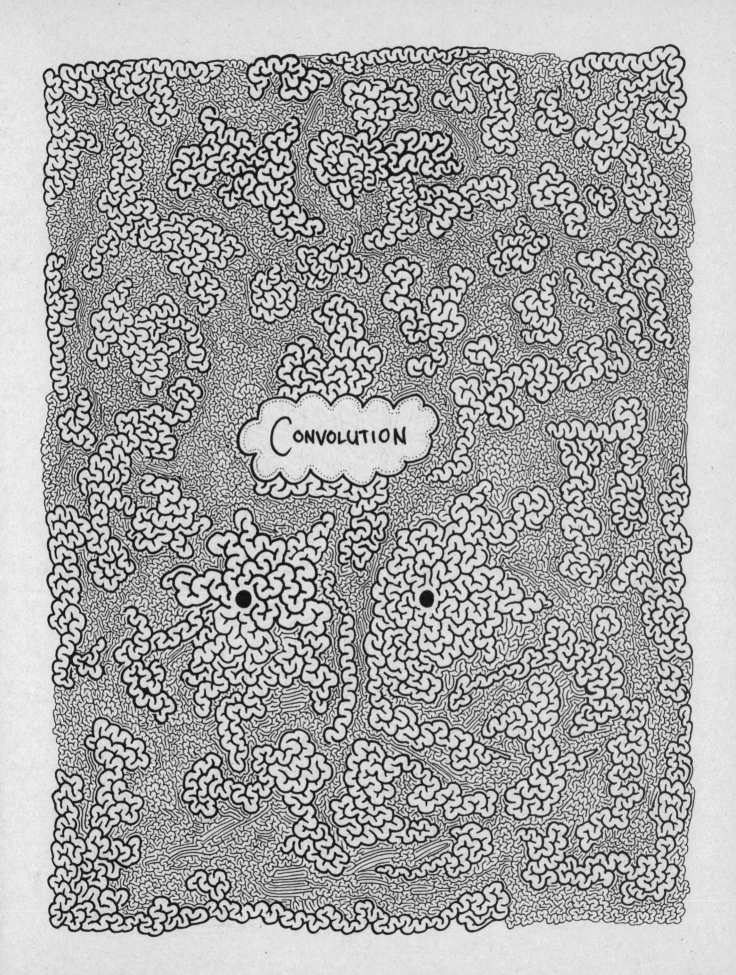

Noodlemania

FINISH

START

the PINK maze

END

START

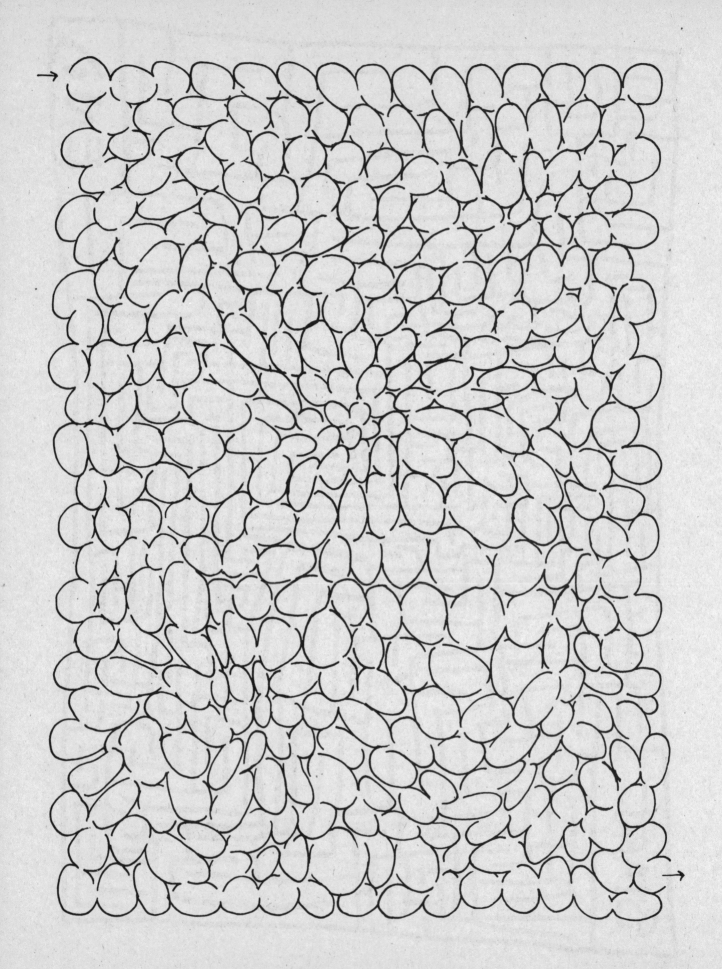

88

Solution page 190

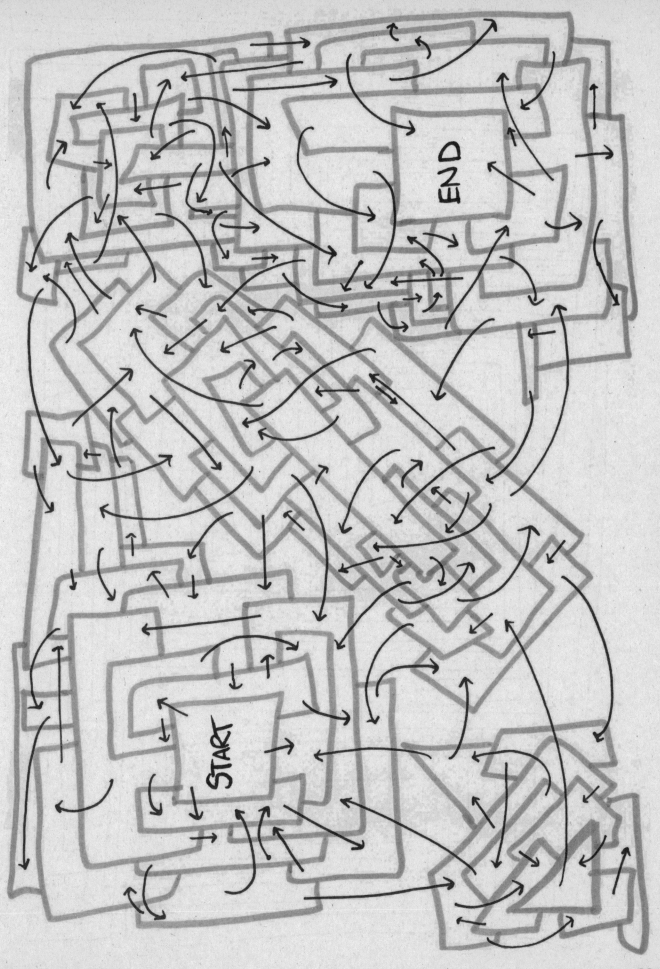

Solution page 191

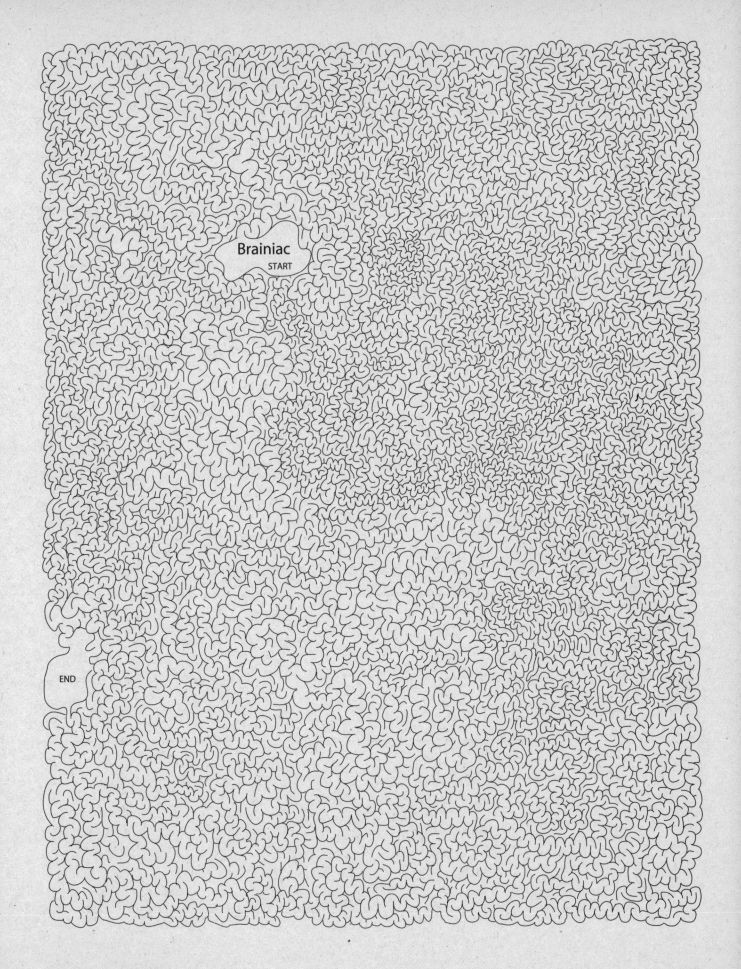

Brainiac

START

END

Chapter 6
3-D
ILLUSIONS

Chapter 6 • Introduction

Perhaps the biggest attraction to our website is from visitors seeking to find truly three-dimensional looking illusions. These mazes make for great brainteasers. They generally require a high degree of aptitude in the way of spatial thinking. Because of this, a relatively small maze can often require a long time to actually solve. Pathways bend and quirk over, under, through, and around behind one another in such a manner as to often leave one completely disoriented. Matthew Locke is to be credited as a true master in the creation of these mazes.

Depth Trap

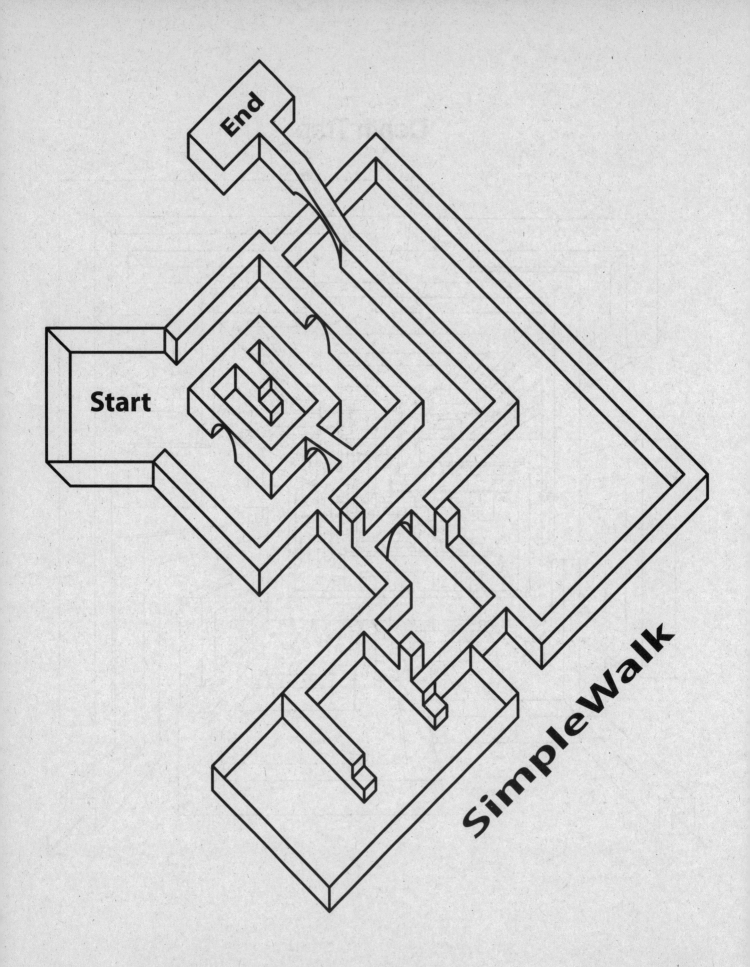

End

Start

SimpleWalk

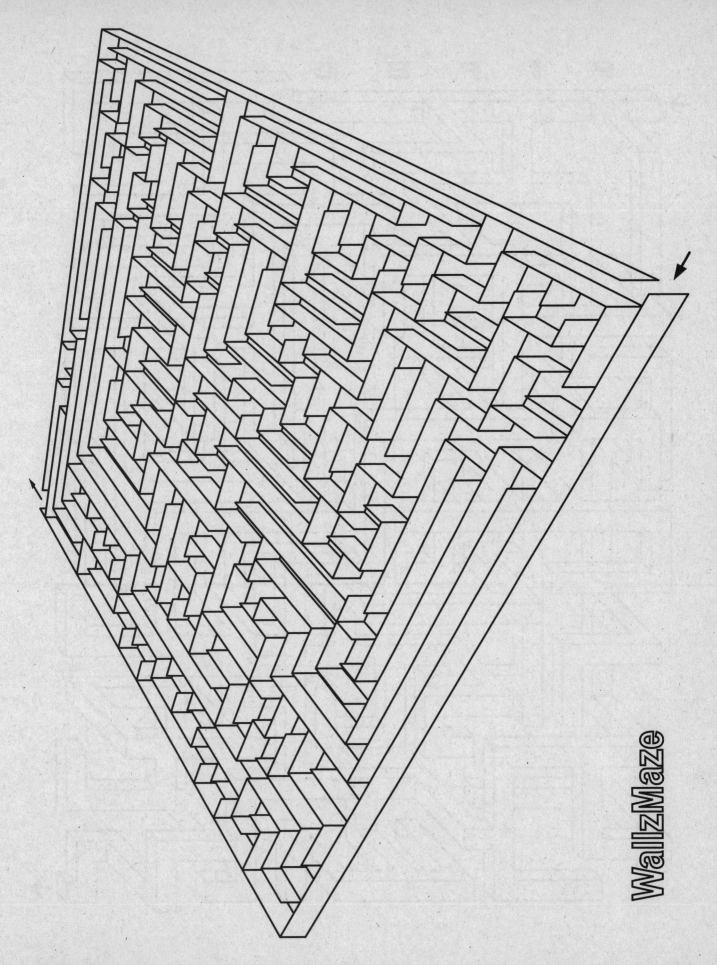

WallzMaze

Solution page 198

LEVELED

VERTI-WALL

Solution page 197

Pillar Slide

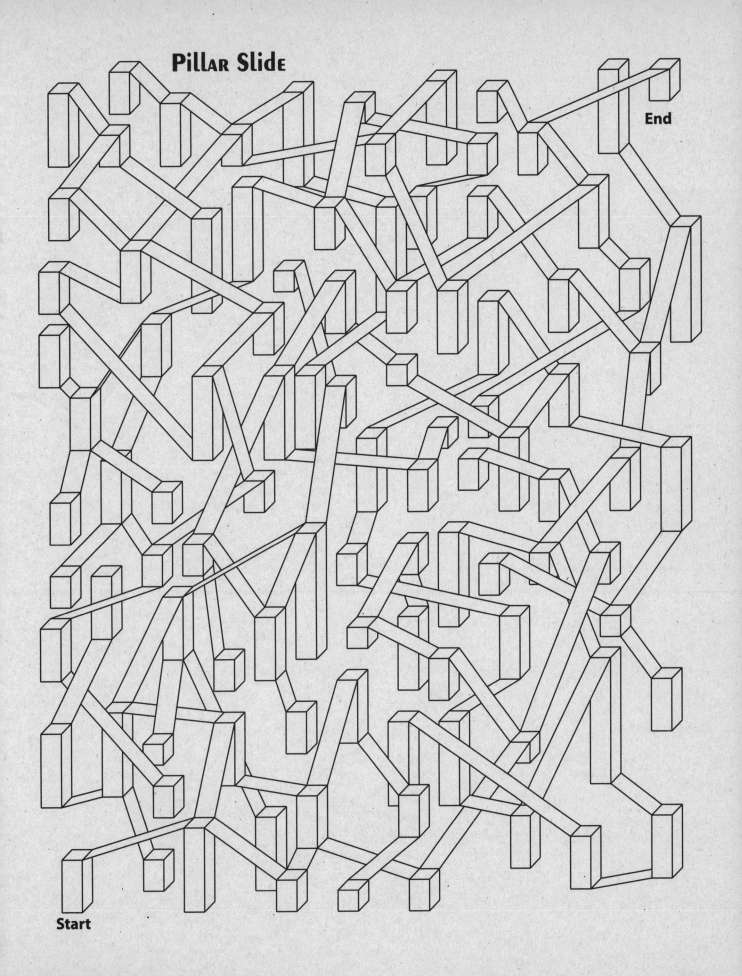

End

Start

Chapter 7

MegaMaze
MISCELLANY

Chapter 7 • Introduction

If you are a true maze connoisseur or just looking for some exceptionally unique and difficult mazes, then this chapter is for you. Beware, for in order to solve the mazes contained on these pages, your patience may be tried. Your mental mettle will be pushed to the limit.

The unforgiving but highly energetic jumping mazes in this chapter are among the most confusing mazes ever published. To solve these mazes, proceed from start to finish box by box along the arrows only in the designated directions. Do not exit any boxed area except along one of these arrows. The "Cardinals" and "Leafy Trail" mazes present slight variations on this theme, travel being from grid square to grid square and from leaf to leaf, respectively.

The tile mazes are another type of original, though somewhat less difficult, maze in this chapter. In the tile mazes, travel from start to finish from shape to shape of the same color through only a shape's sides or edges. Diagonal travel, to a shape not adjacent but kitty-corner, is not permitted.

The electric spaghetti mazes display a frenzied jumble of passages that mask a truly convoluted solution. Travel over and under pathways in order to proceed through these mazes.

As a very unique approach to the 3-D pattern mazes, there are included in this chapter certain rare crystalline constructs. These icy mazes befuddle the mind and distract the eye. Though over and under travel is required for these mazes, be careful not to slide off of their slippery edges since outright flying is still not permitted. When you find yourself accidentally traversing the abyss, a complete restart should be required.

And, you will even find a surprisingly difficult time in attempting to solve "Shocked," as well — this, despite the fact that it is merely a 2-D pattern-styled maze.

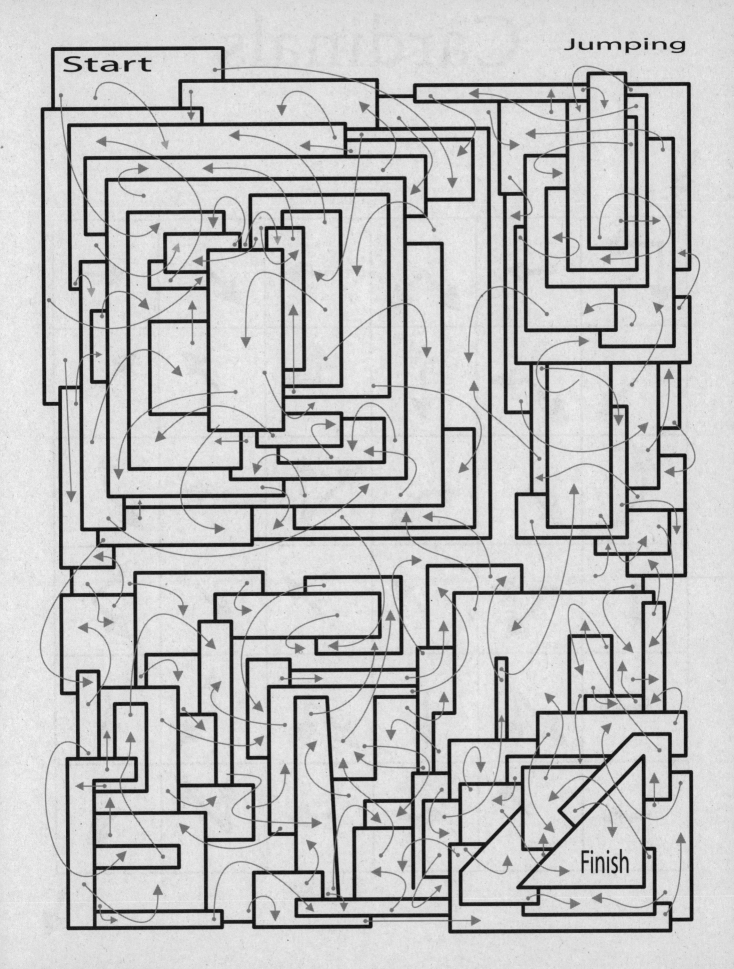

Start

Finish

Cardinals

Solution page 200

Start

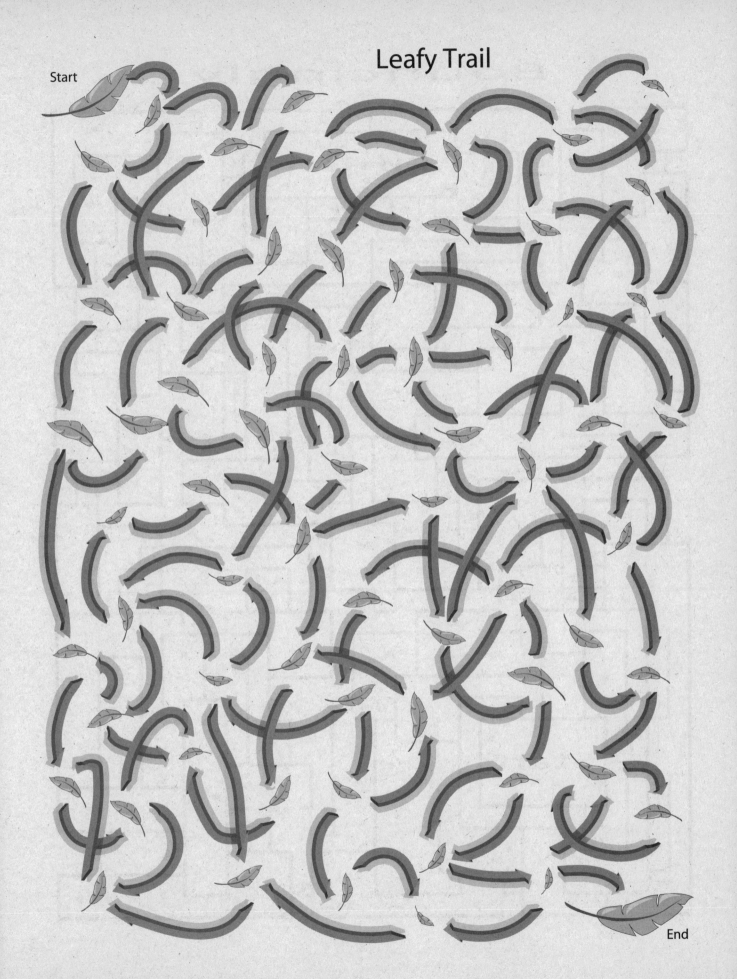

End

Bouncingly

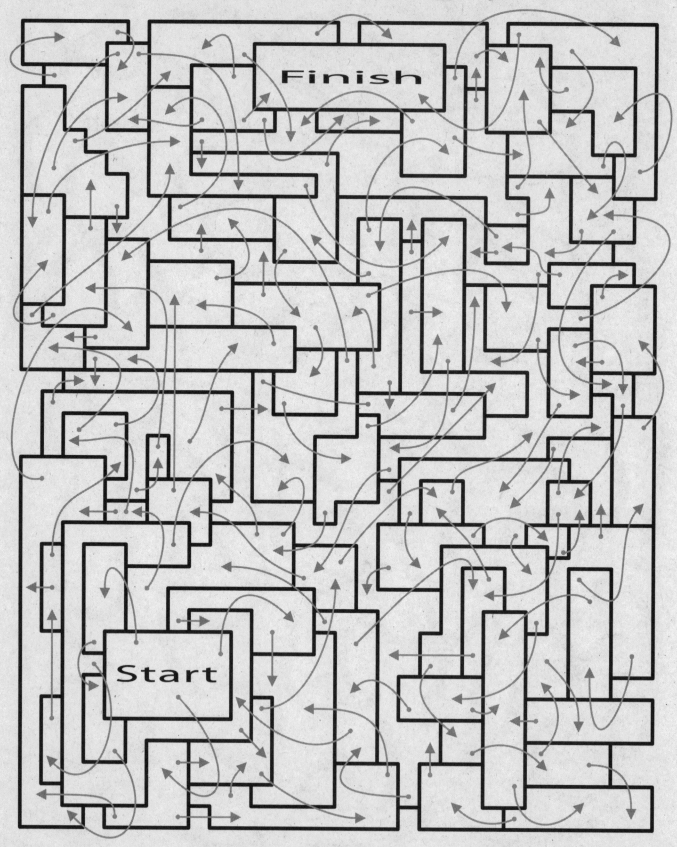

Finish

Start

Solution page 201

Cubezoid Duplicity

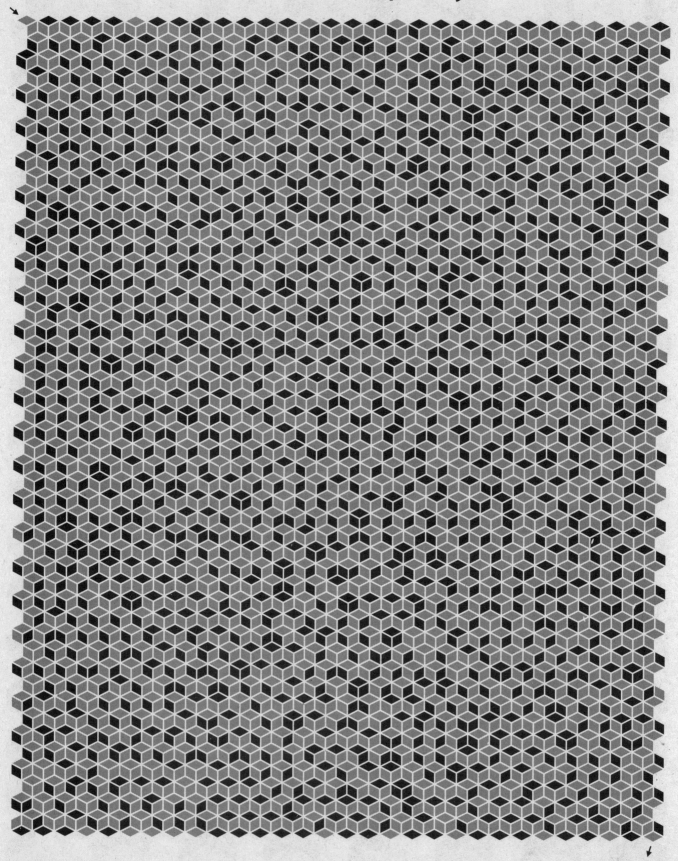

Solution page 203

CubeShelves

Solution page 204

Electroid

START

END

114

Solution page 205

Shocked

Electri-fried

START

END

Solution page 206

Crystal Road

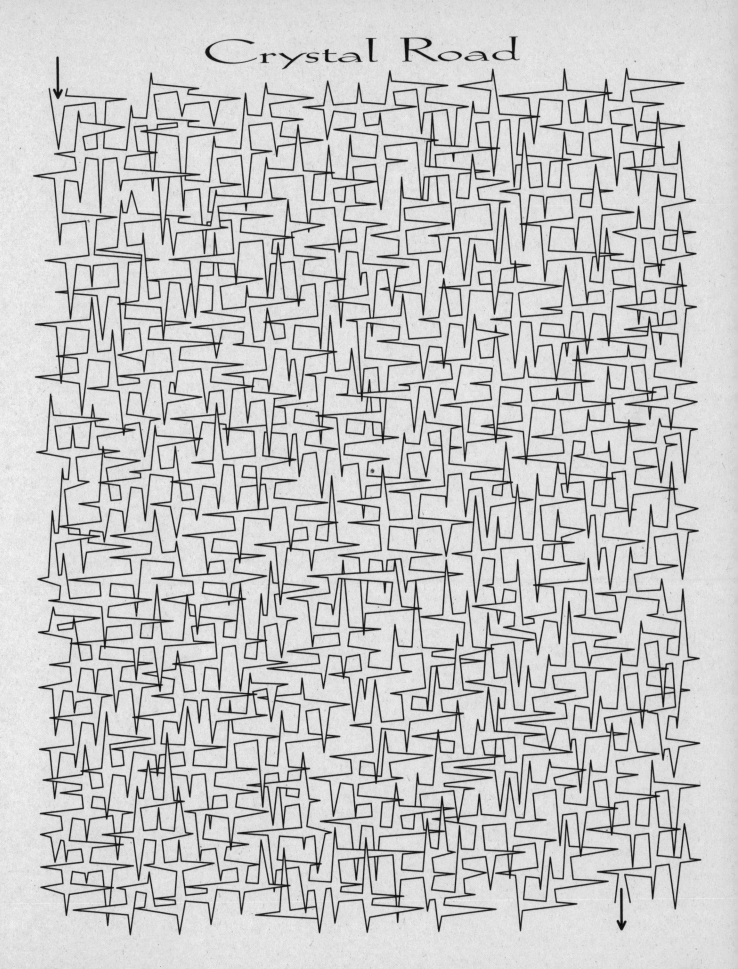

Chapter 8

MODIFICATIONS

ALTERED STATES

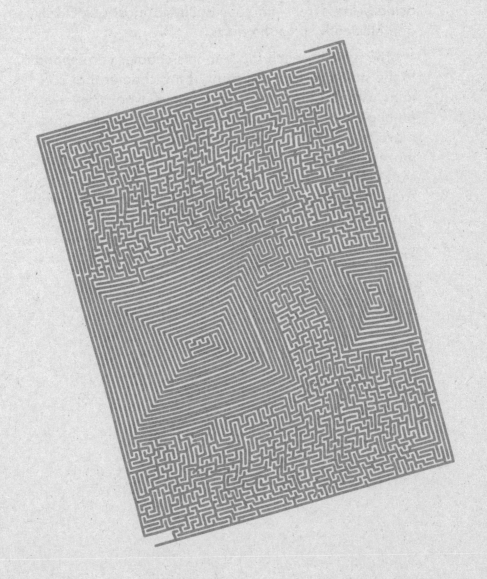

Chapter 8 • Introduction

The final chapter of our *Big Big Book of Mazes* is a mysterious medley of crazy creations. It is comprised of many elements that you may recognize throughout the book, but these mazes are presented in a fashion that is often quite unorthodox. Though these mazes may resemble certain others in the preceding chapters, you will find that their solutions will require a complete rework. In fact, it will probably be the case that your familiarity with the similar counterpart of a "mod" actually interferes with your ability to most objectively and efficiently solve the maze.

The rules for each maze in this chapter correspond to the stated rules at the front of the chapter that contains similar mazes of that same type. However, among these new mazes are included several "line-maze" styles that are new to this chapter. To solve these mazes, merely proceed along each line tube from the start until you arrive at the finish mark. The linear passages of these mazes do not overlap and under/over travel will not be required.

start

finish

JelloWarp

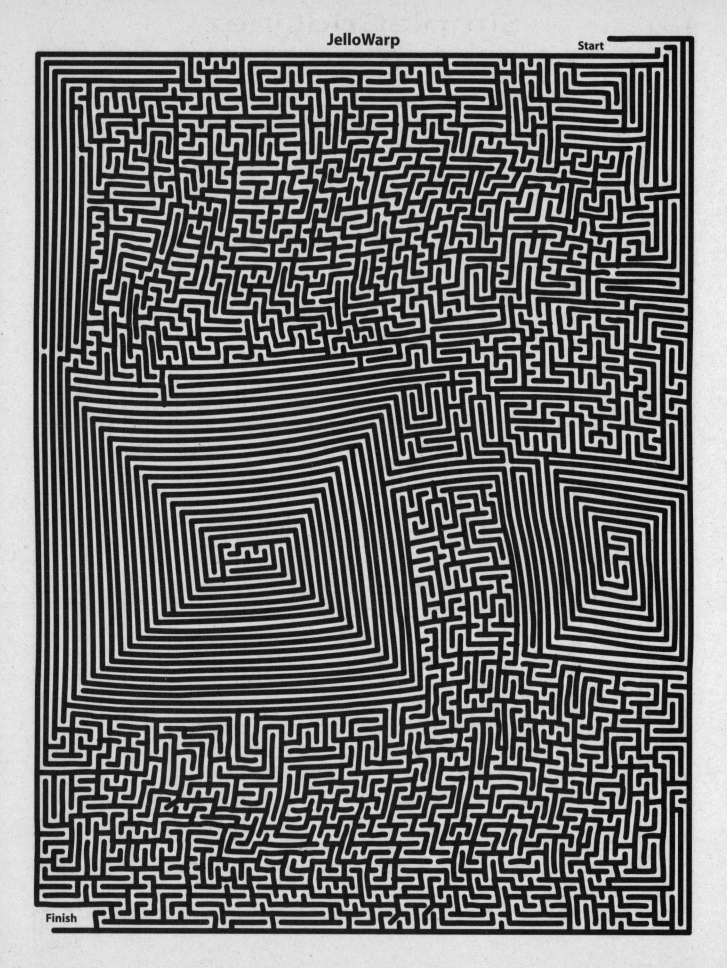

Finish

WallzMaze

Solution page 208

Circuitry

HexWarp

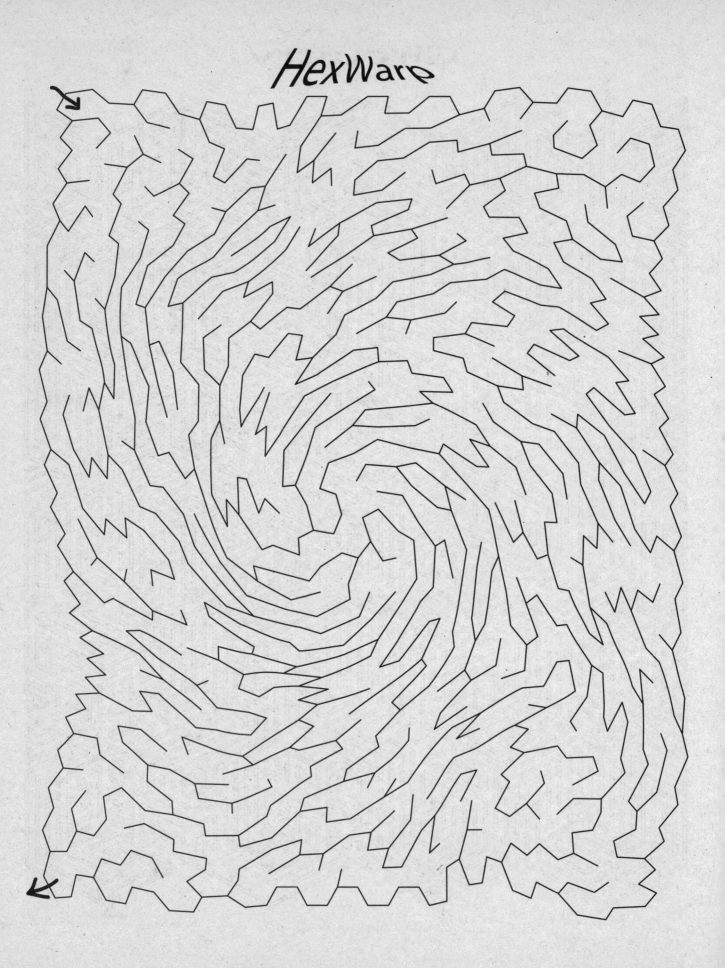

Solution page 212

HEXXED

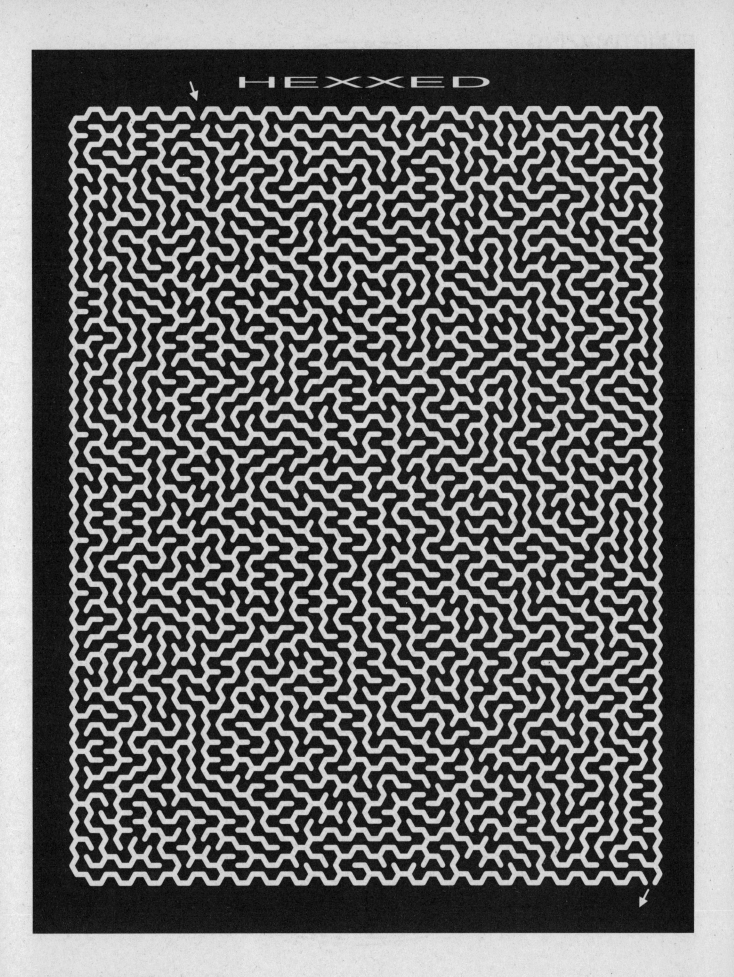

ELLIPTIMAZING

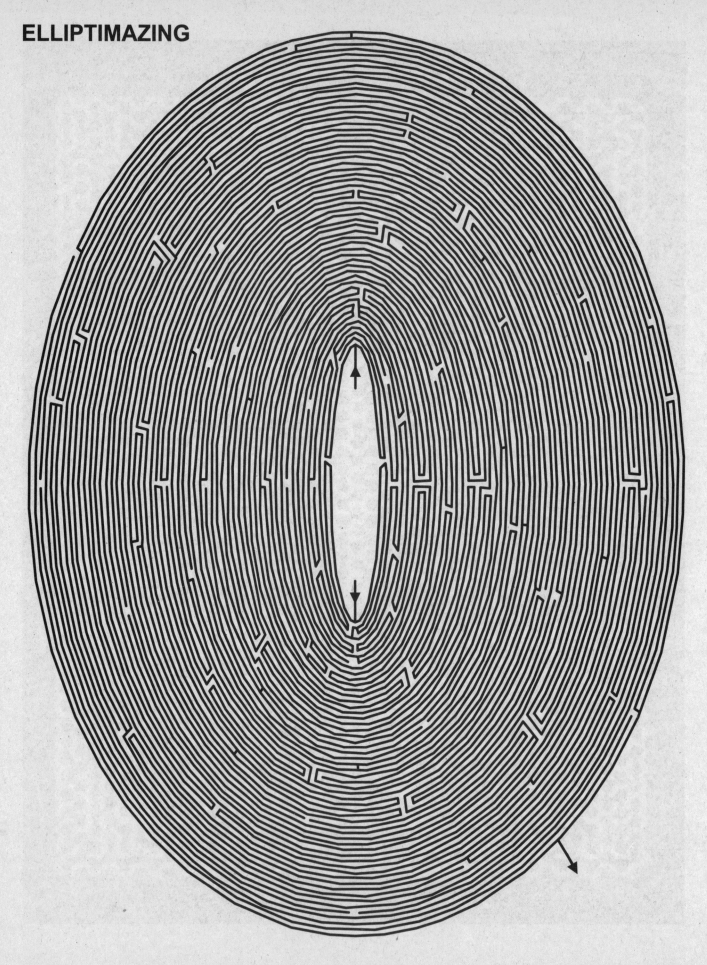

Gridlocked

Finish

wormlinez

Solution page 213

WarpDrains

Solution page 213

Elliptoroid LineMaze

Finish

Hexa**Bulge**

Electric Flower

Solution page 218

CRAGGISH

Rubble Trubble

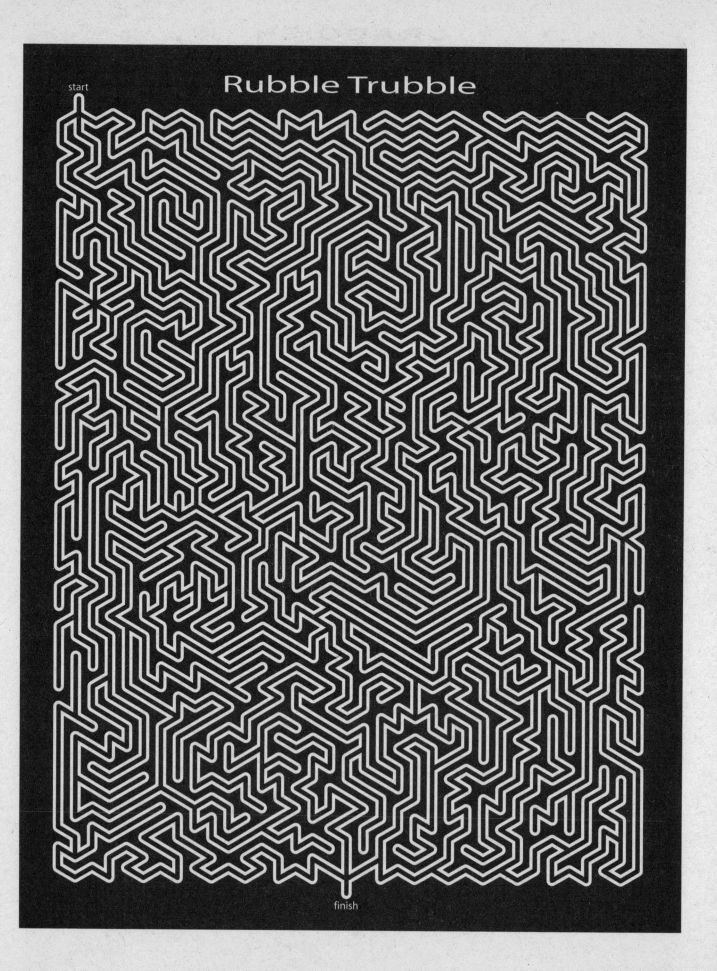

start

finish

Solution page 220

Bubble Swirl

start

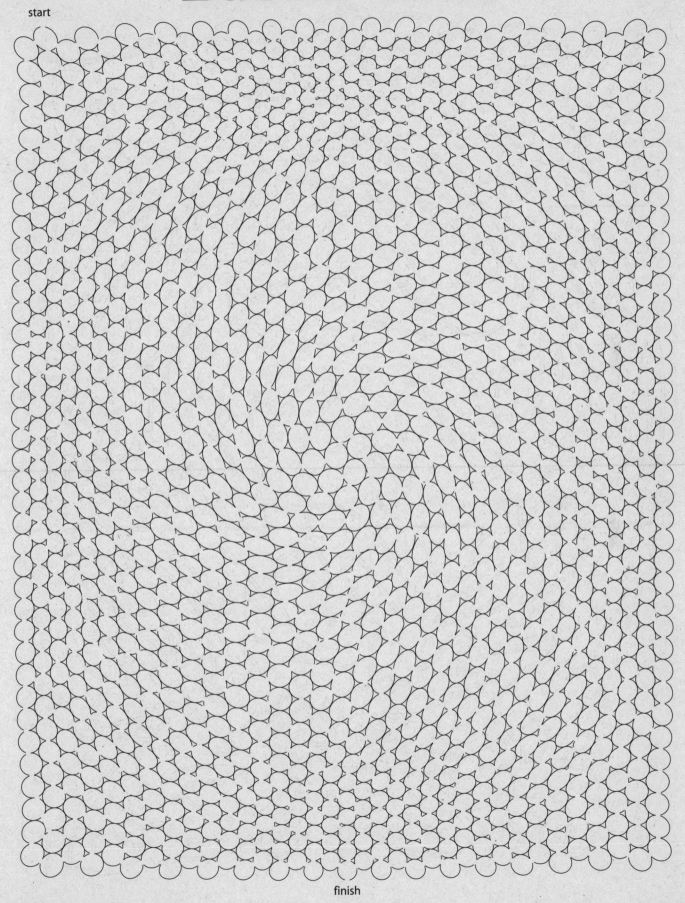

finish

Spaghetti Bulge

finish

Solution page 221

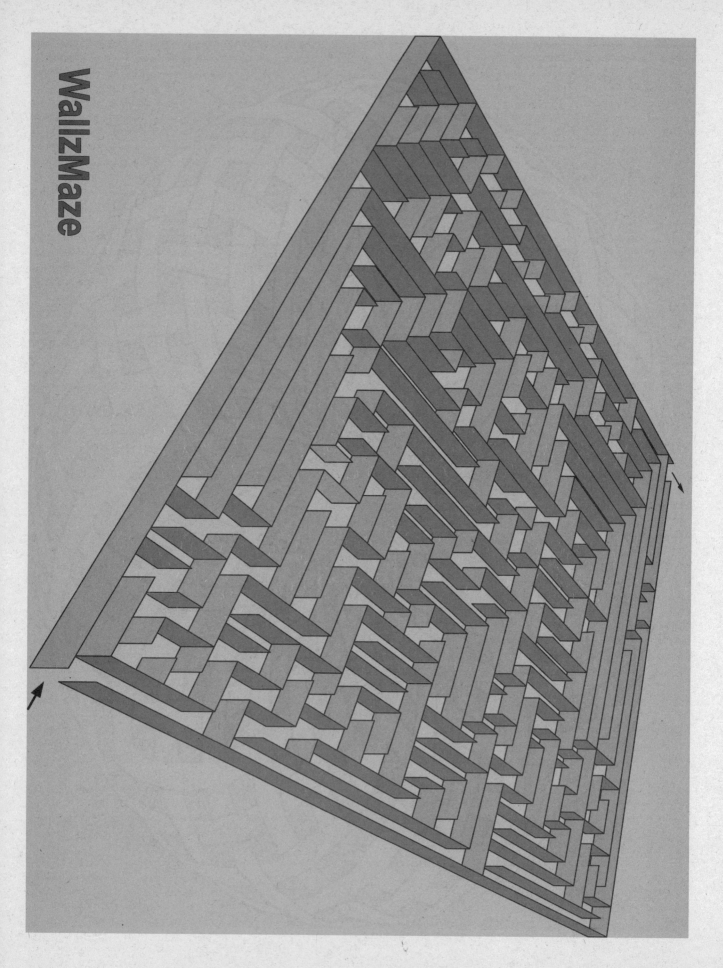

Solution page 223

GREAT GRIDS

SimpleGrid

start

finish

HEXMAZE

start

finish

144

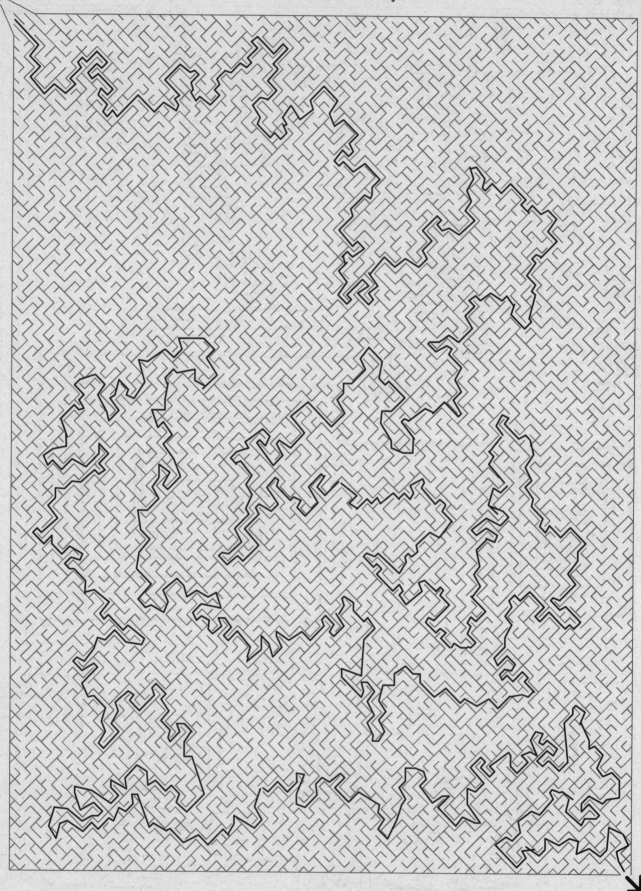

--DIGITIZED--

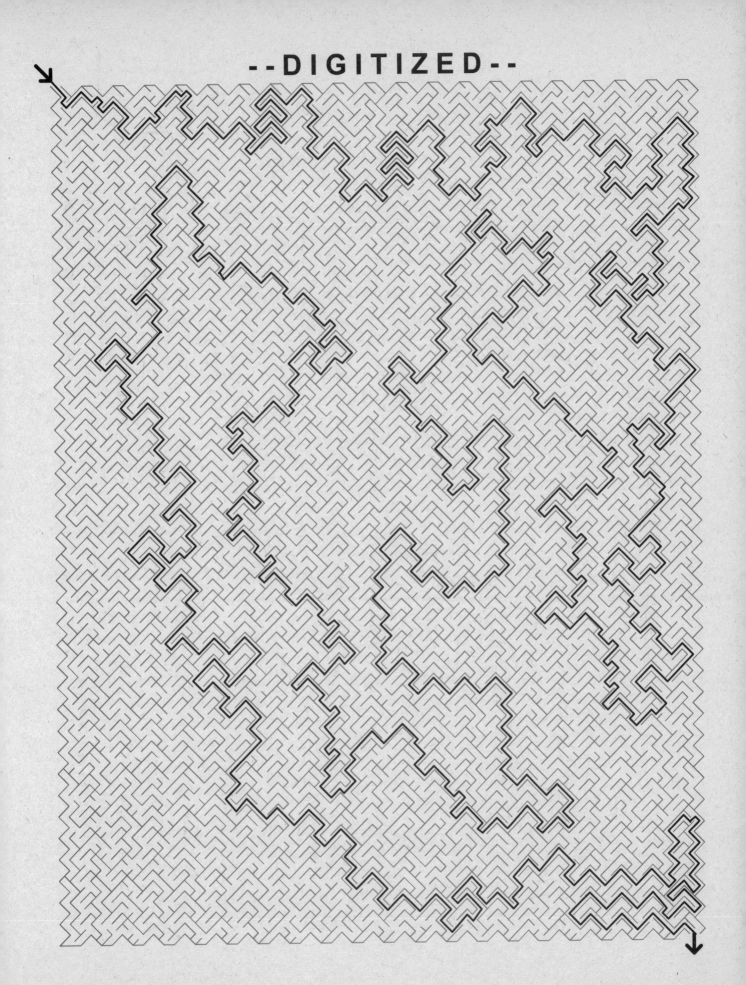

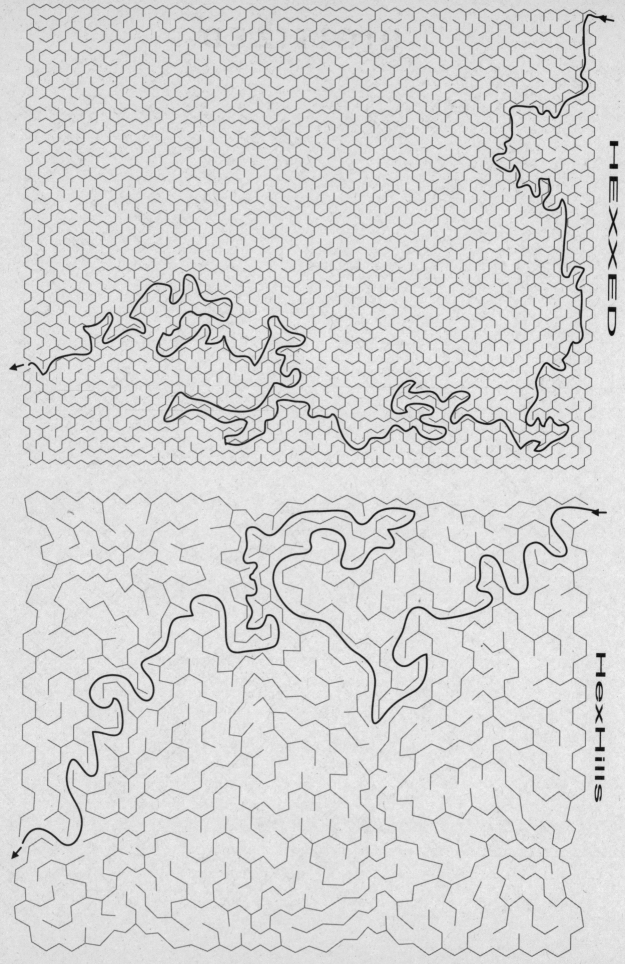

HEXXED

HexHills

Hex Vortex

BubbleHex

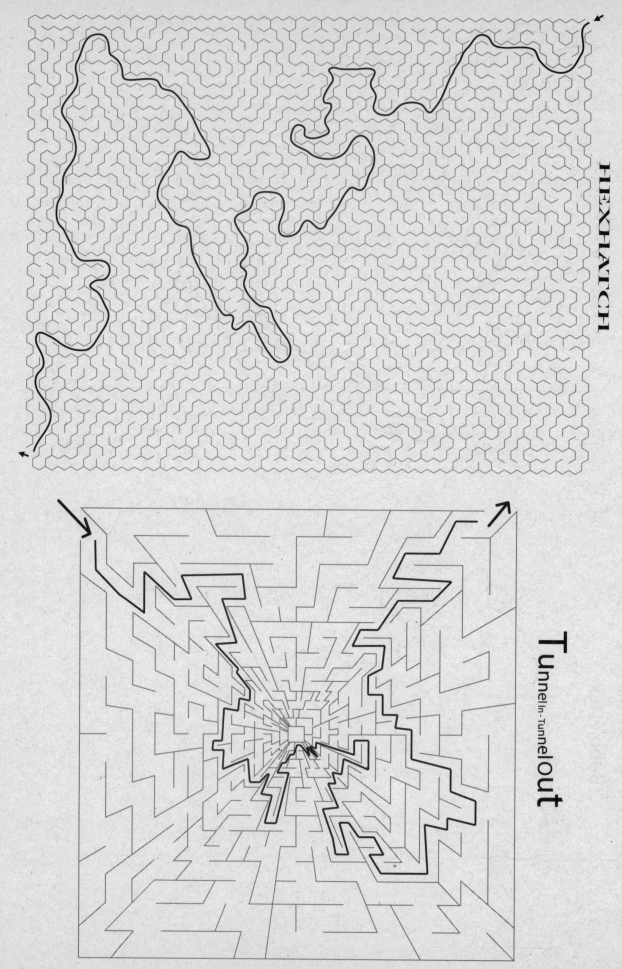

HEXHATCH

Tunnel in - Tunnel out

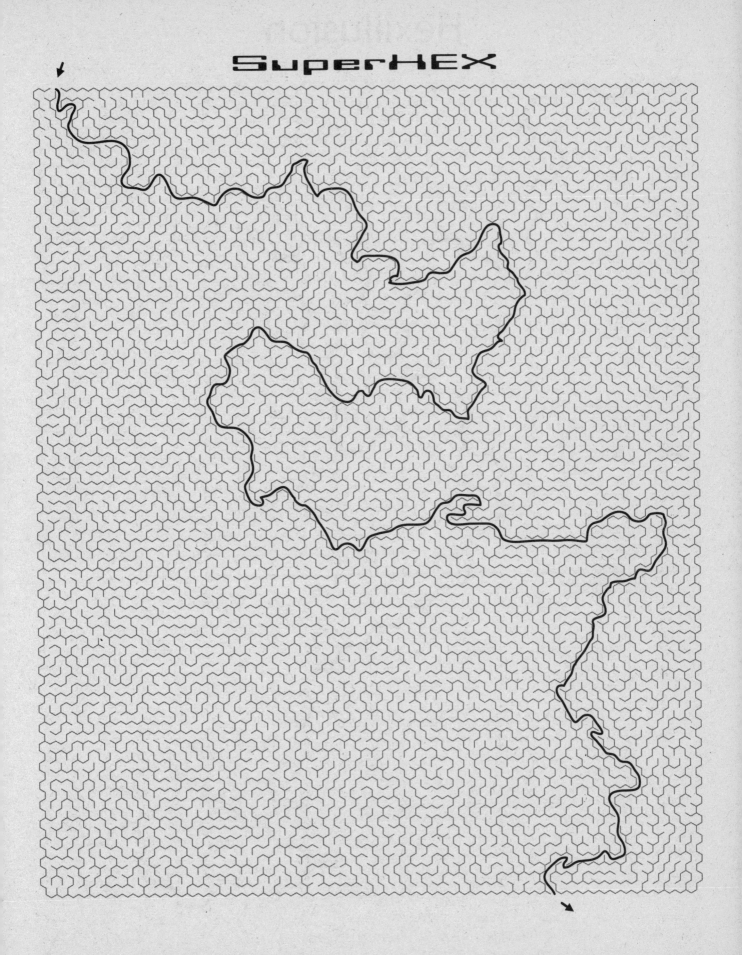

Hexillusion

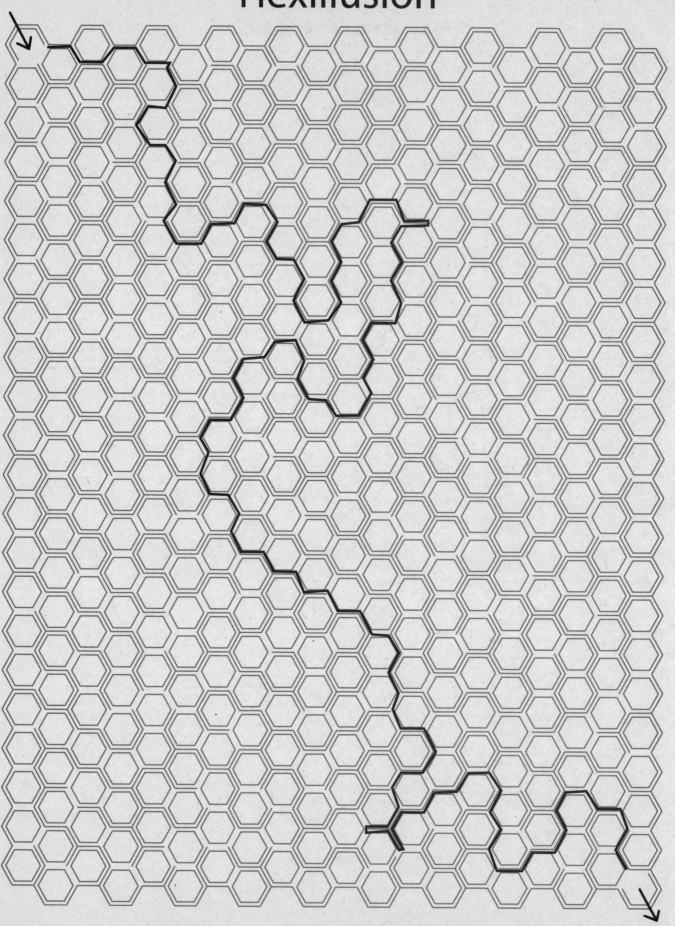

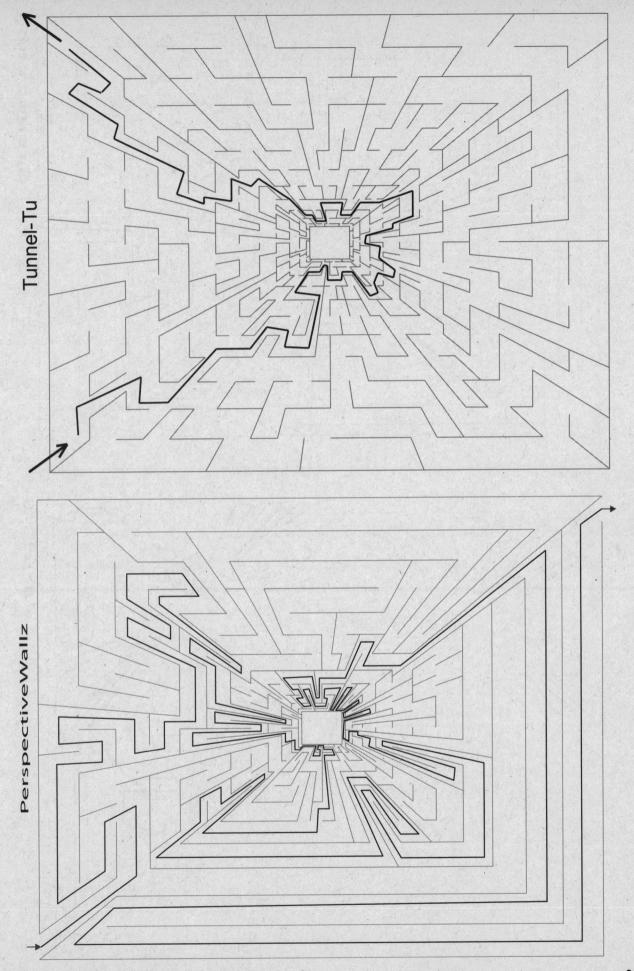

Tunnel-Tu

PerspectiveWallz

153

Start

Finish

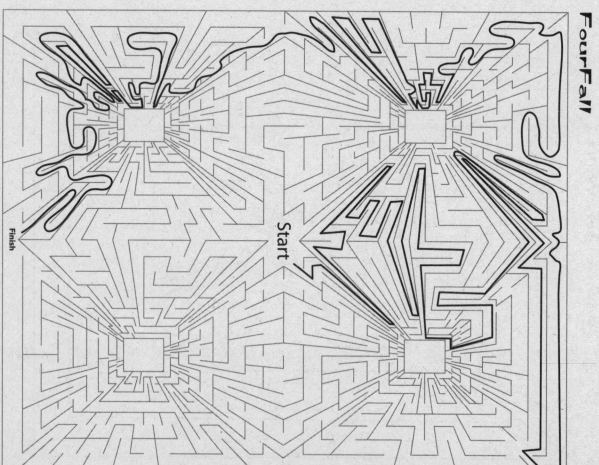

CubesGrid

Dimensional Grid

155

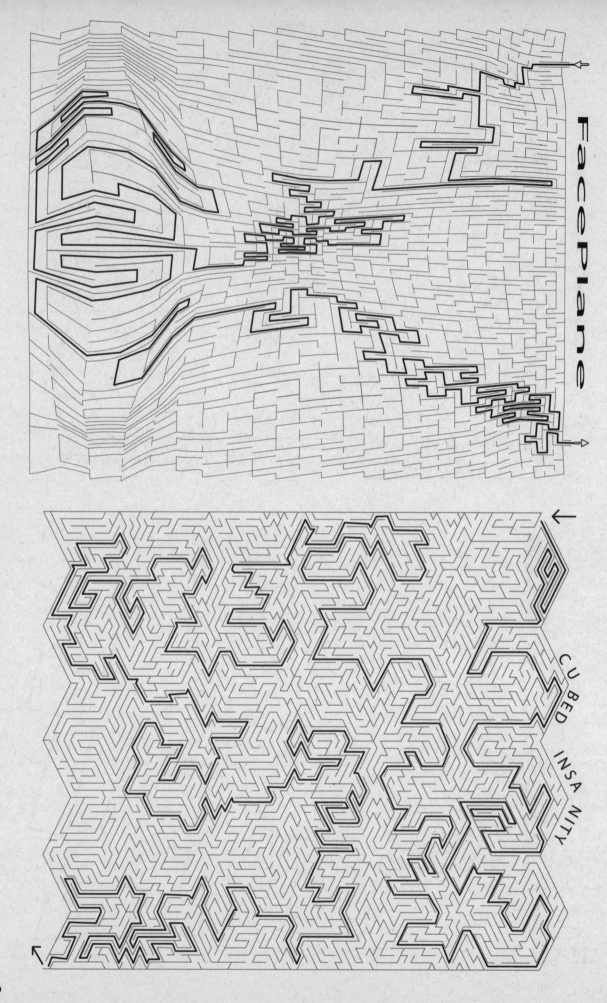

FacePlane

CUBED INSANITY

Five Points of Death

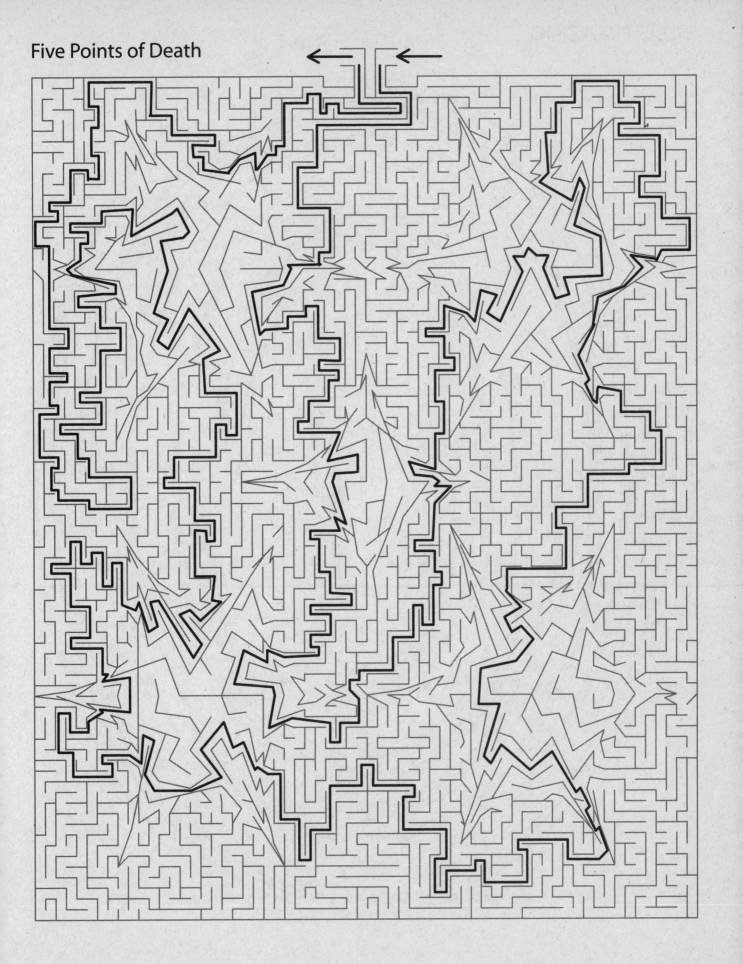

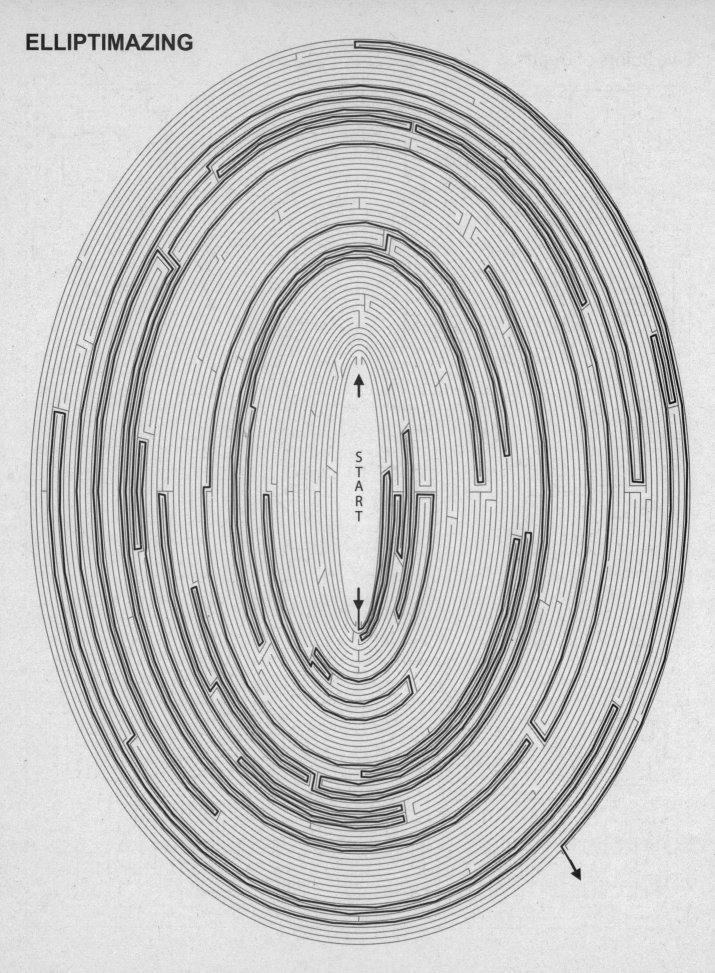

START

DESIGN WARPS

LineZoid

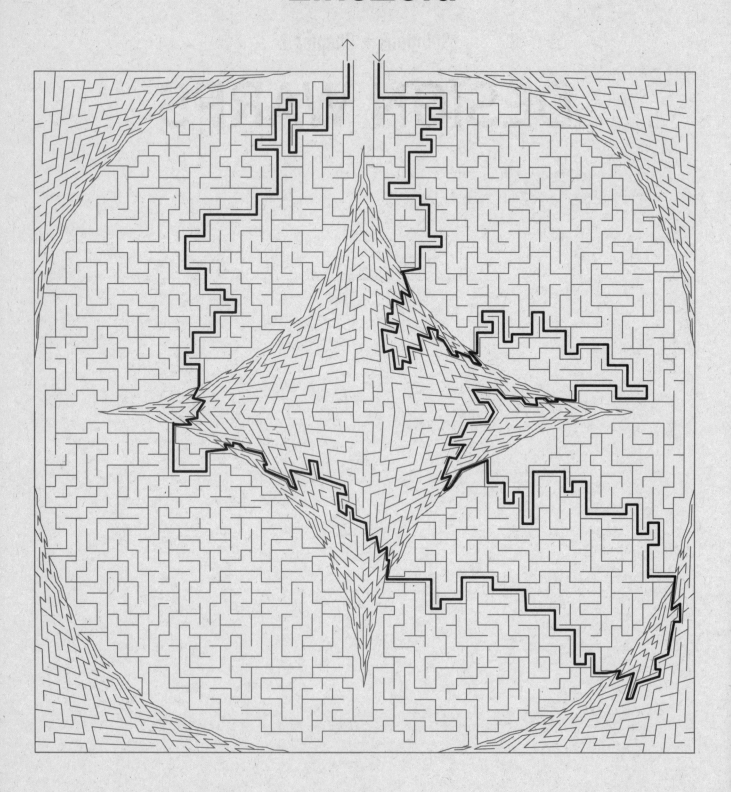

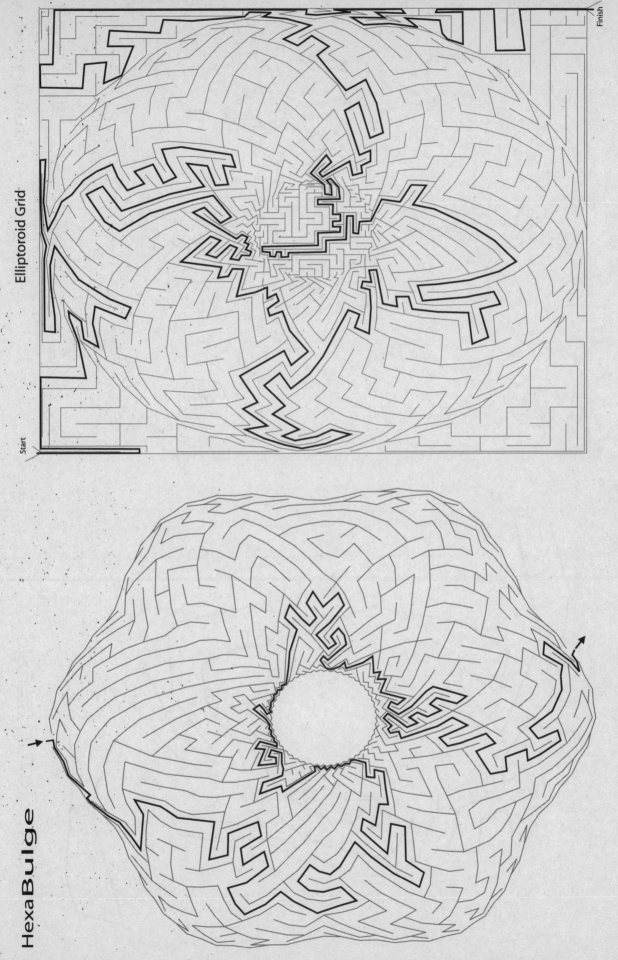

Elliptoroid Grid

Start

HexaBulge

161

Wormhole

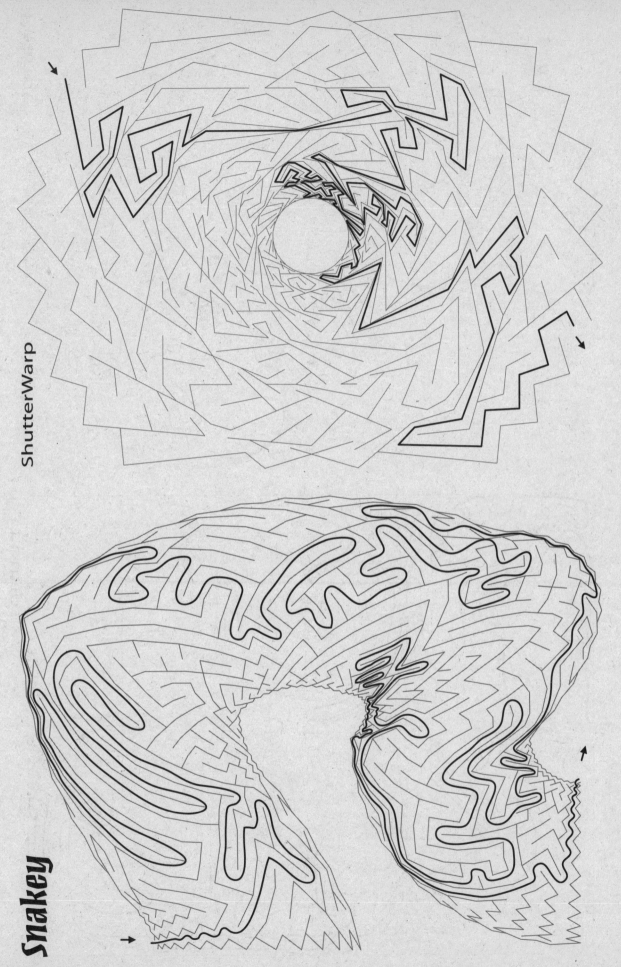

ShutterWarp

Snakey

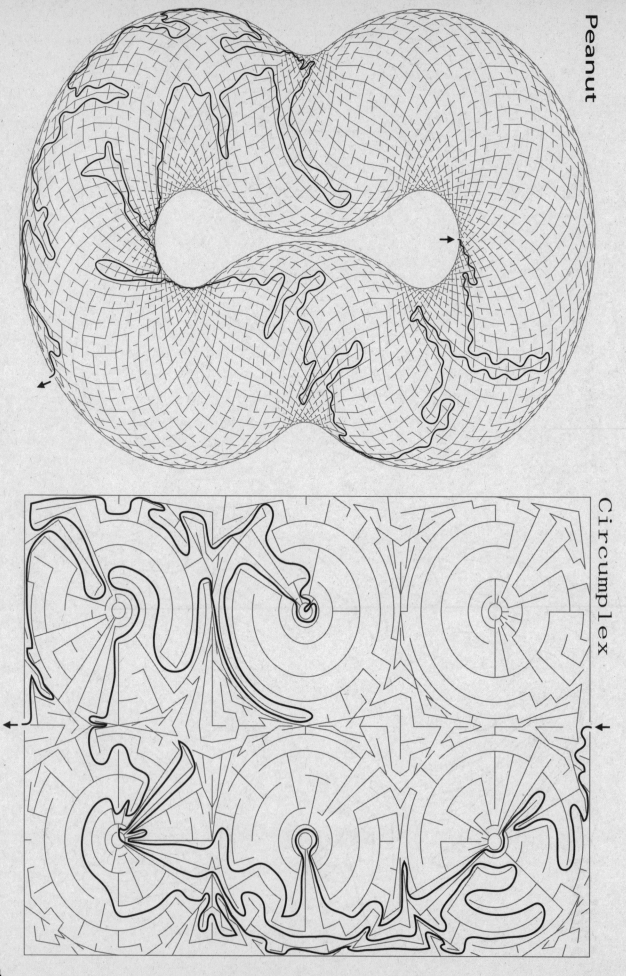

Circumplex

164

HexaFlower

TRITOR INTERLEAVE

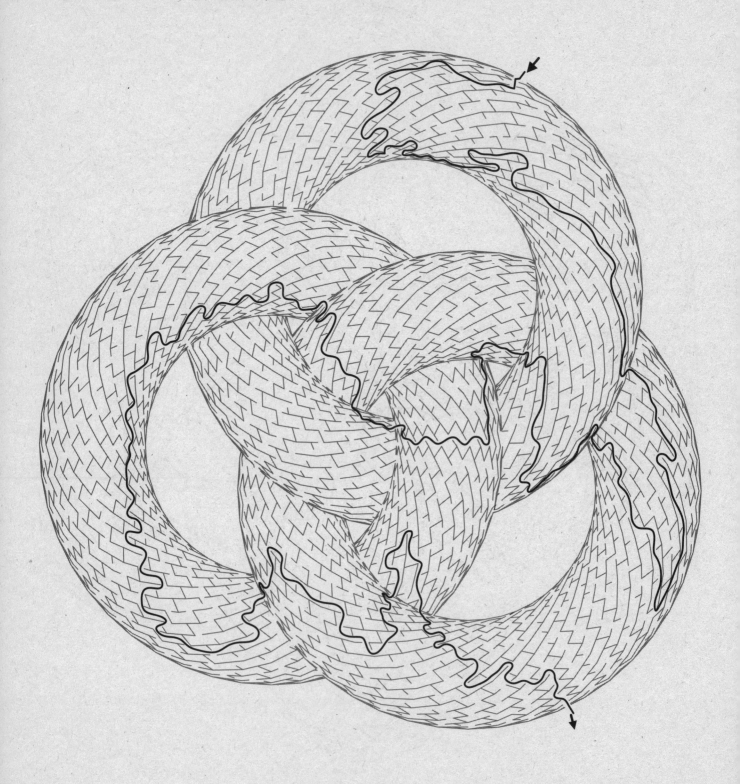

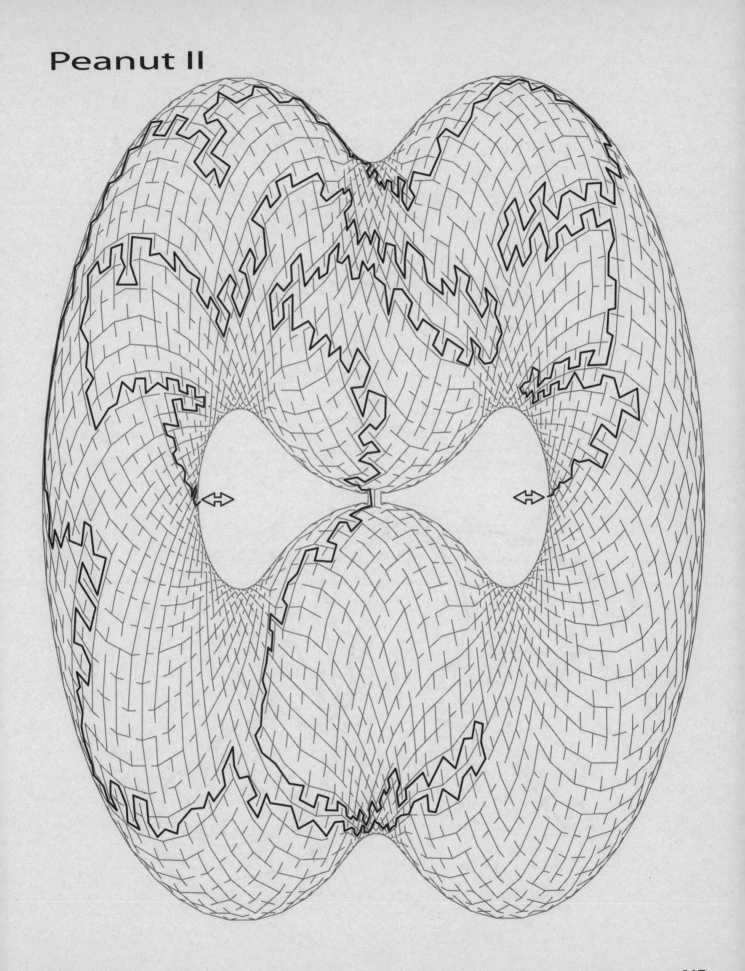

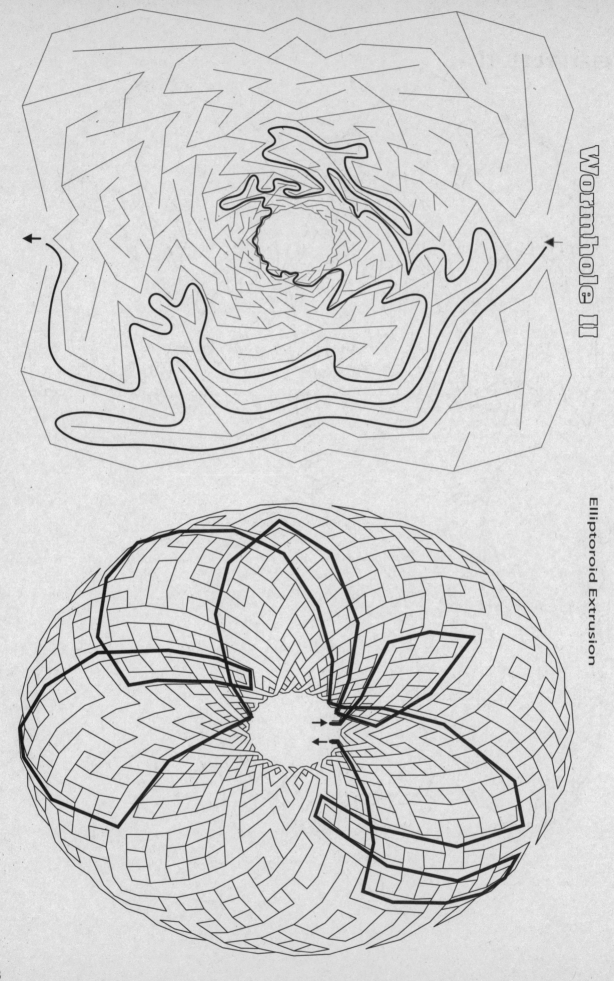

Elliptoroid Extrusion

PATTERNS
ORGANIZED CHAOS

GRIDLOCK

CUBICAL DEPRESSION

HEXISTIC

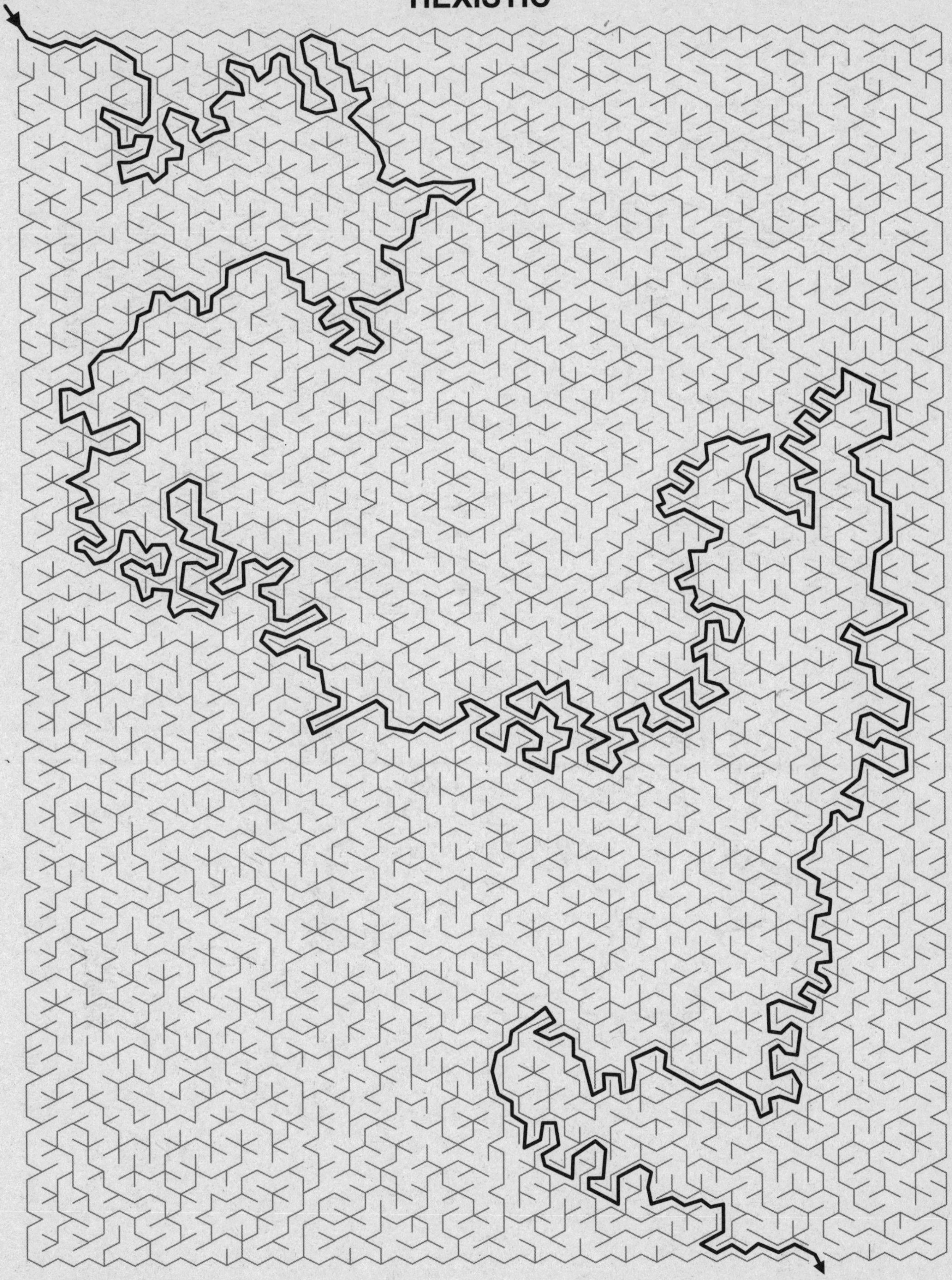

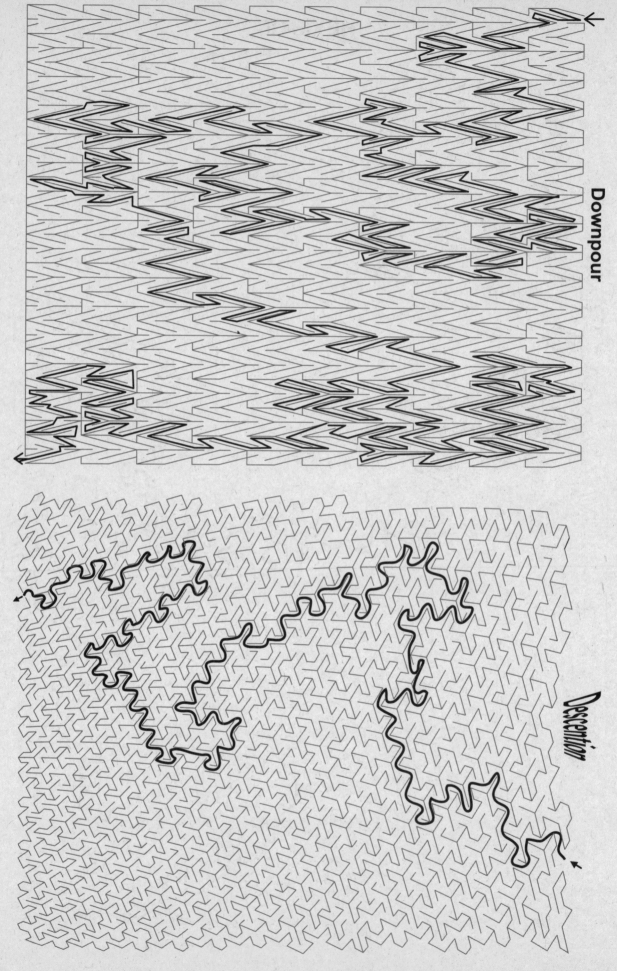

Downpour

Descentior

PentaStarz

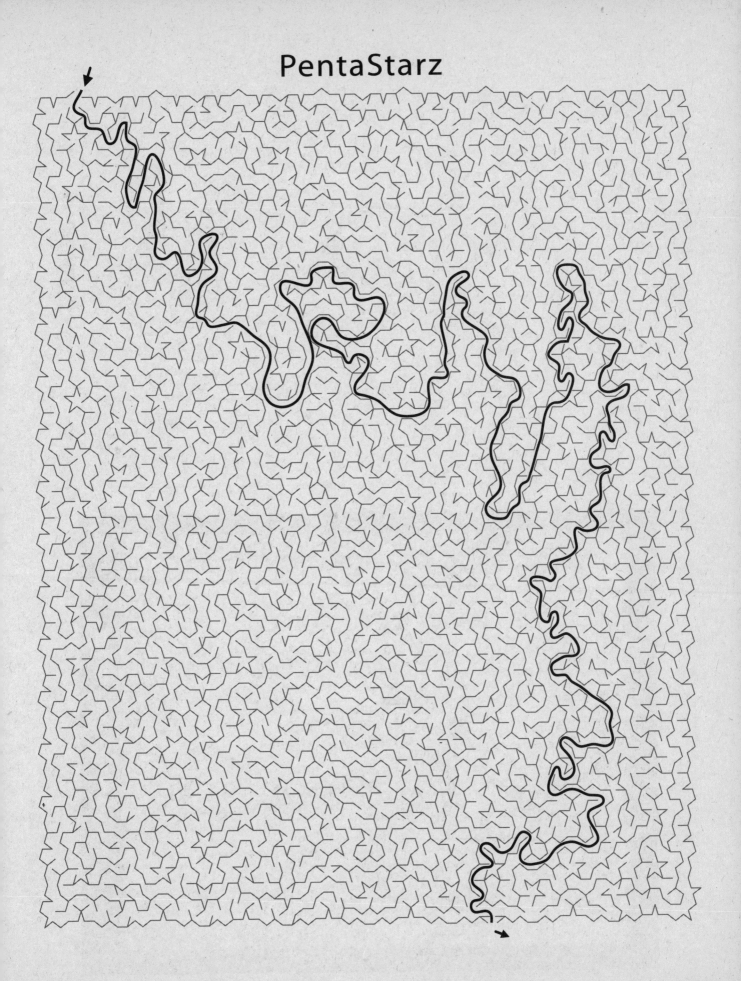

Circle Quirkle

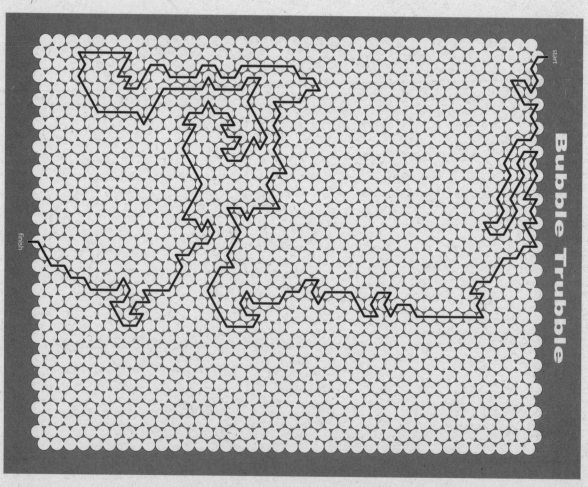

Bubble Trubble

start

finish

174

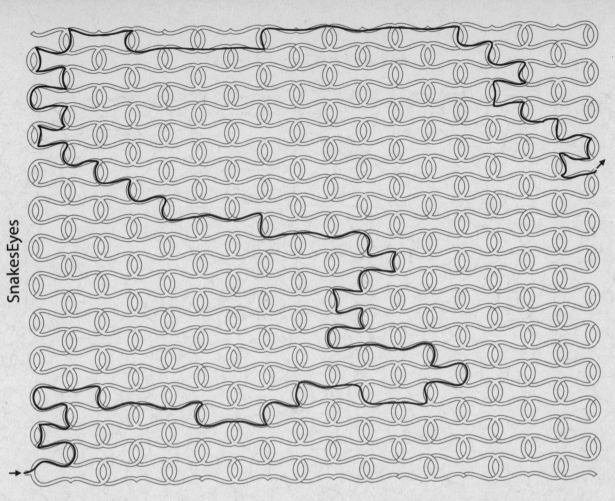

SnakesEyes

Circle Starz

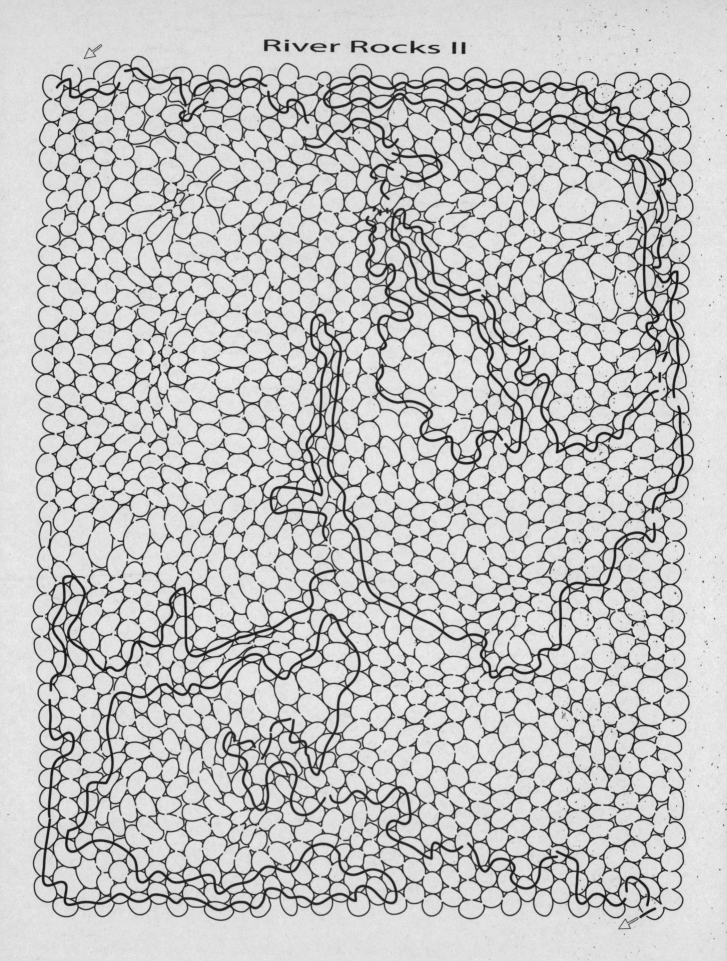

OVERS
AND
UNDERS

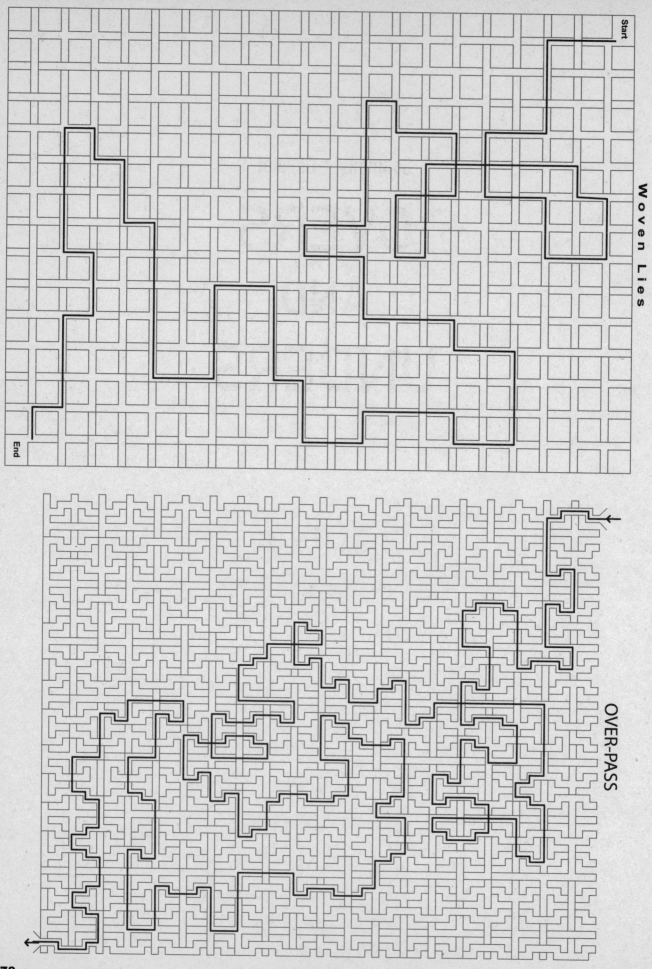

Woven Lies

Start

End

OVER-PASS

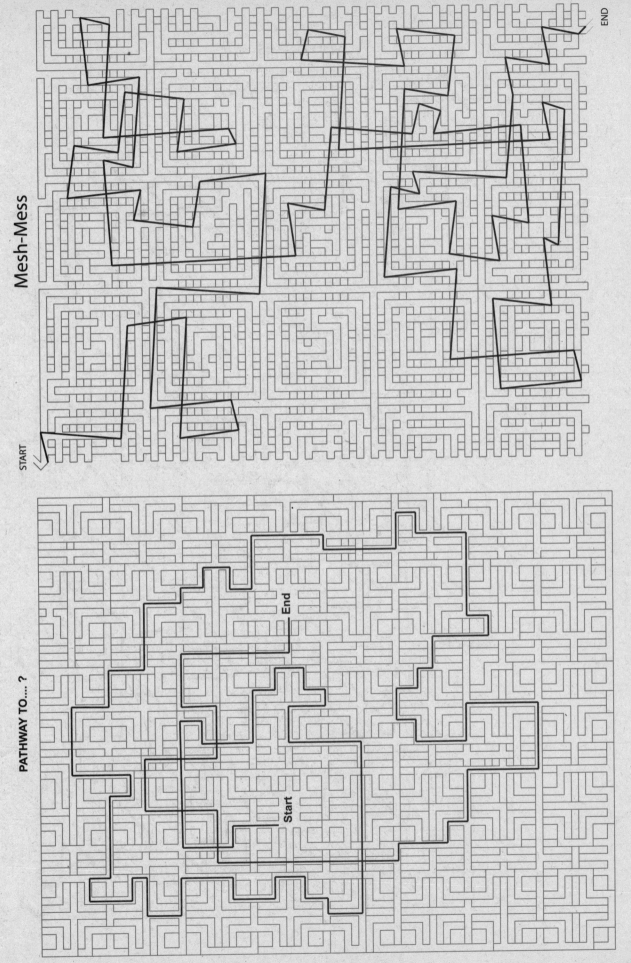

Mesh-Mess

START

END

PATHWAY TO.... ?

End

Start

END

Shape Down

STIX

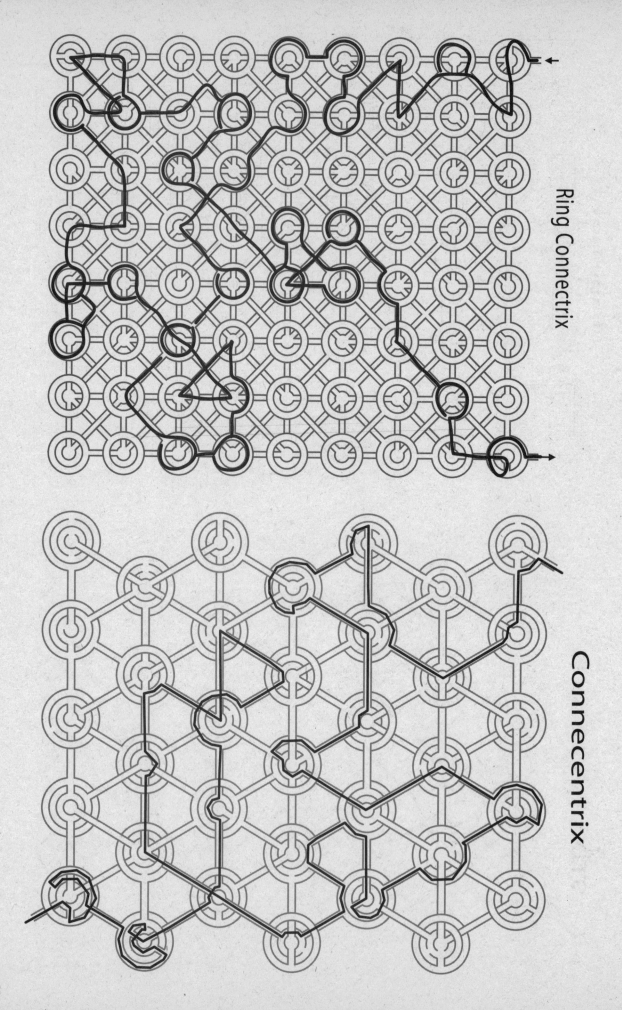

Ring Connectrix

Connecentrix

182

FREEHAND

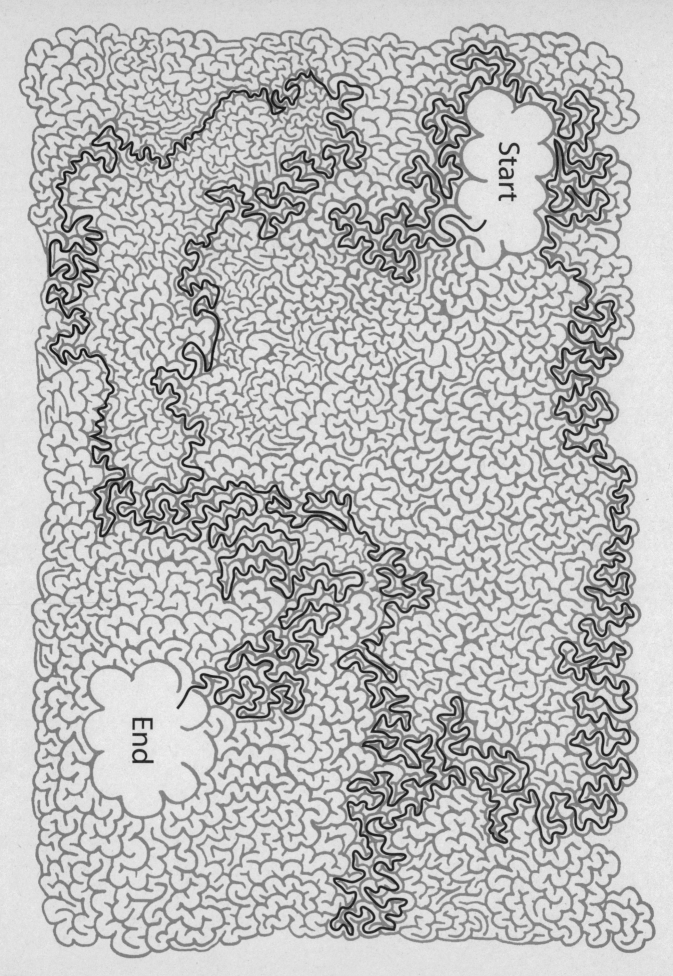

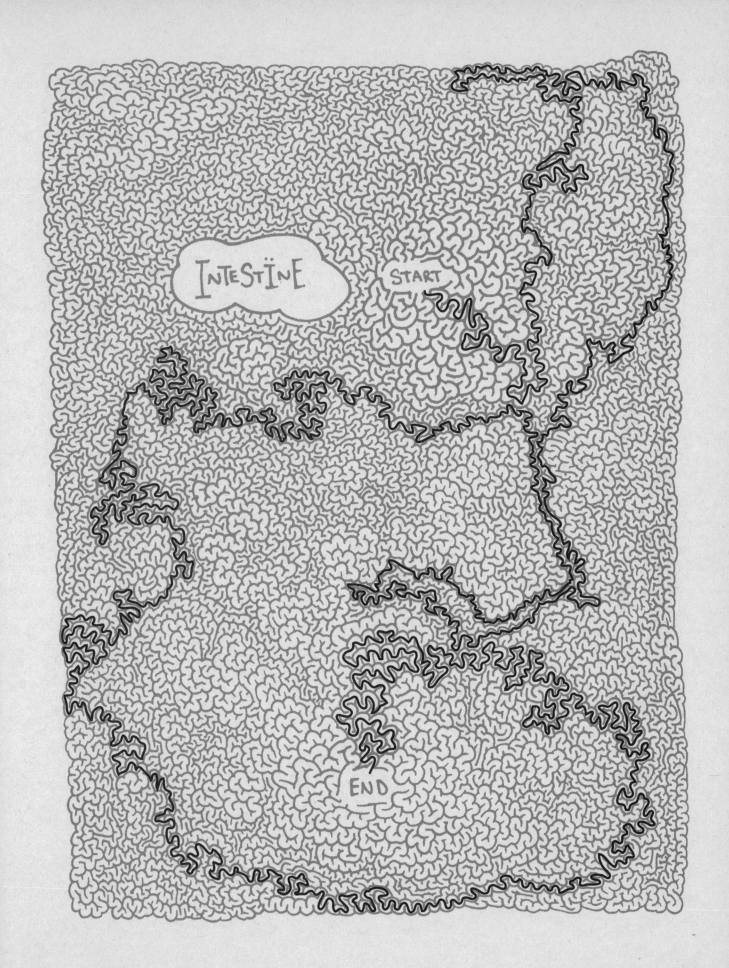

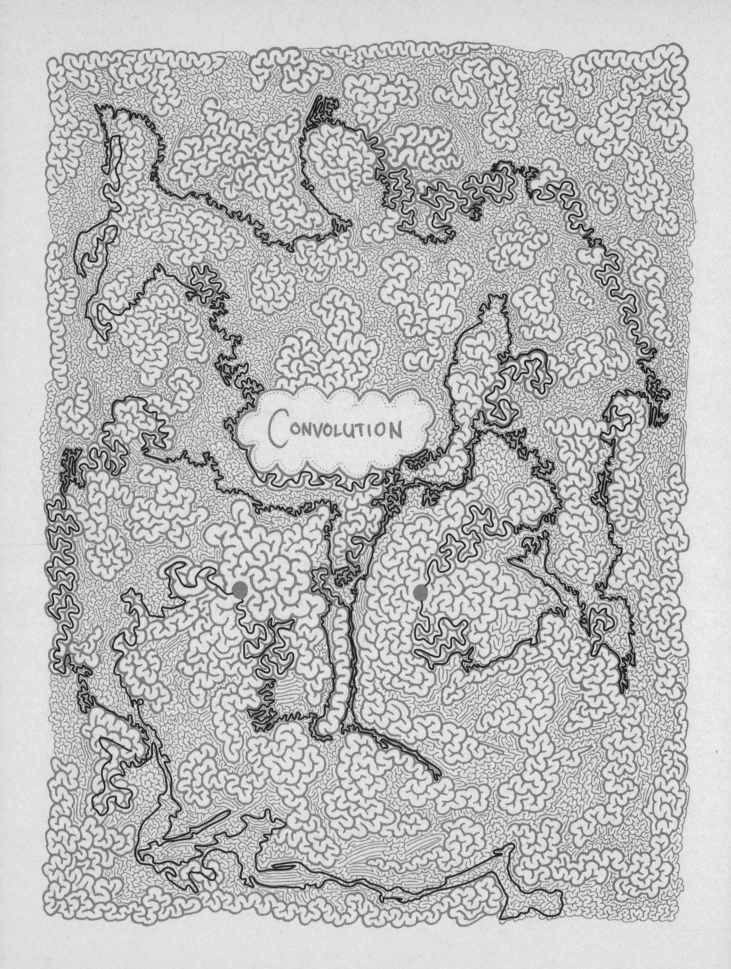

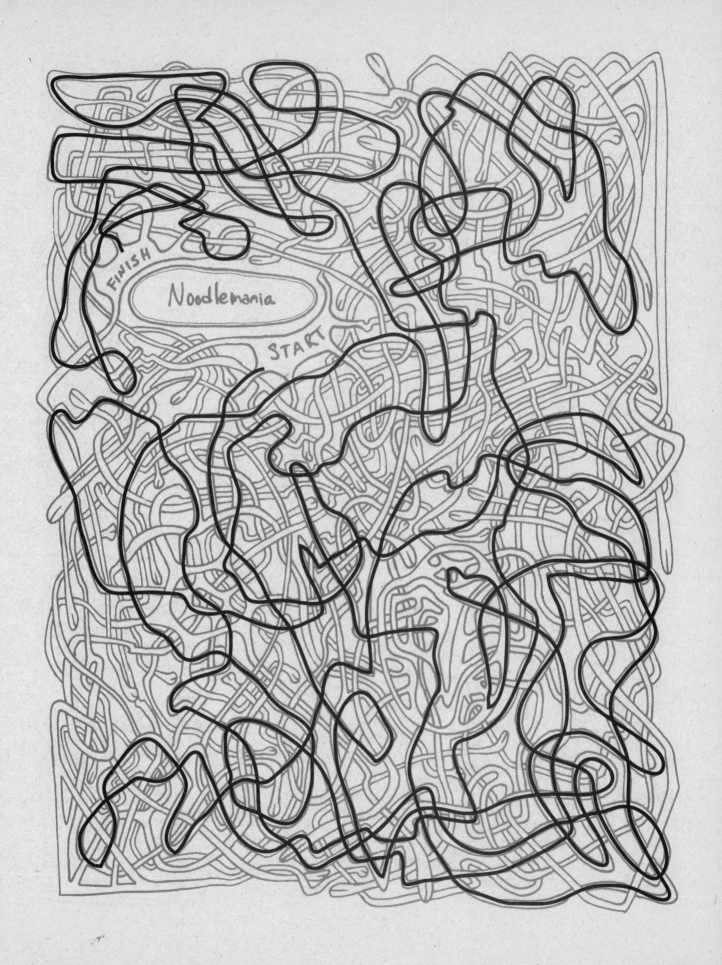

Start

the Stringy Thingy Maze

Finish

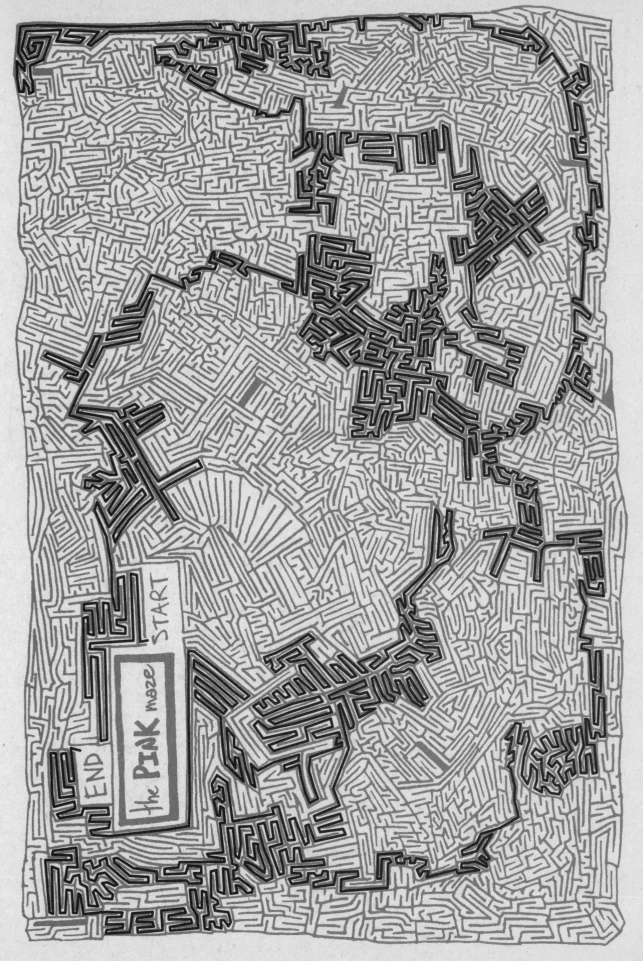

the PiNK maze

START

END

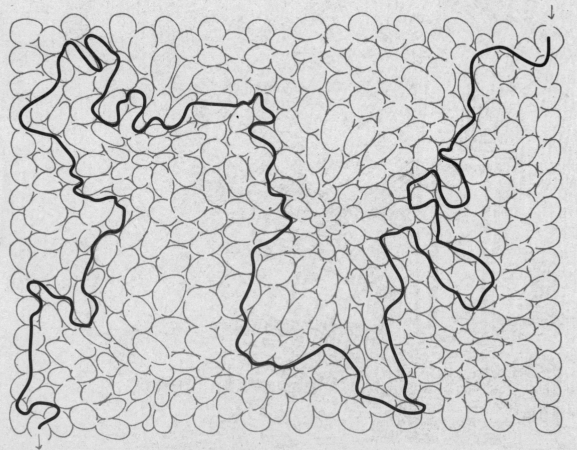

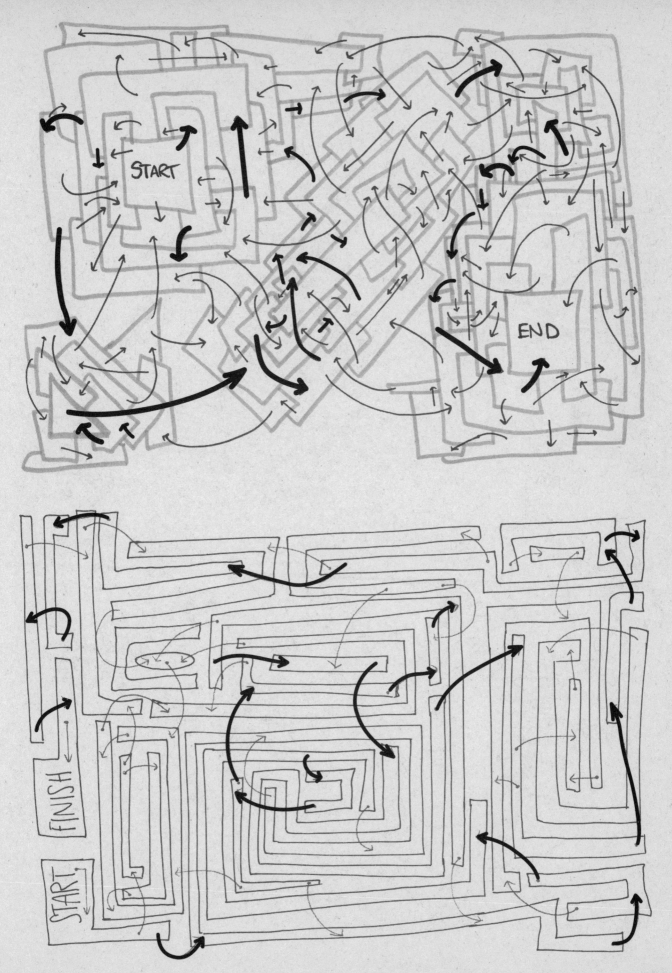

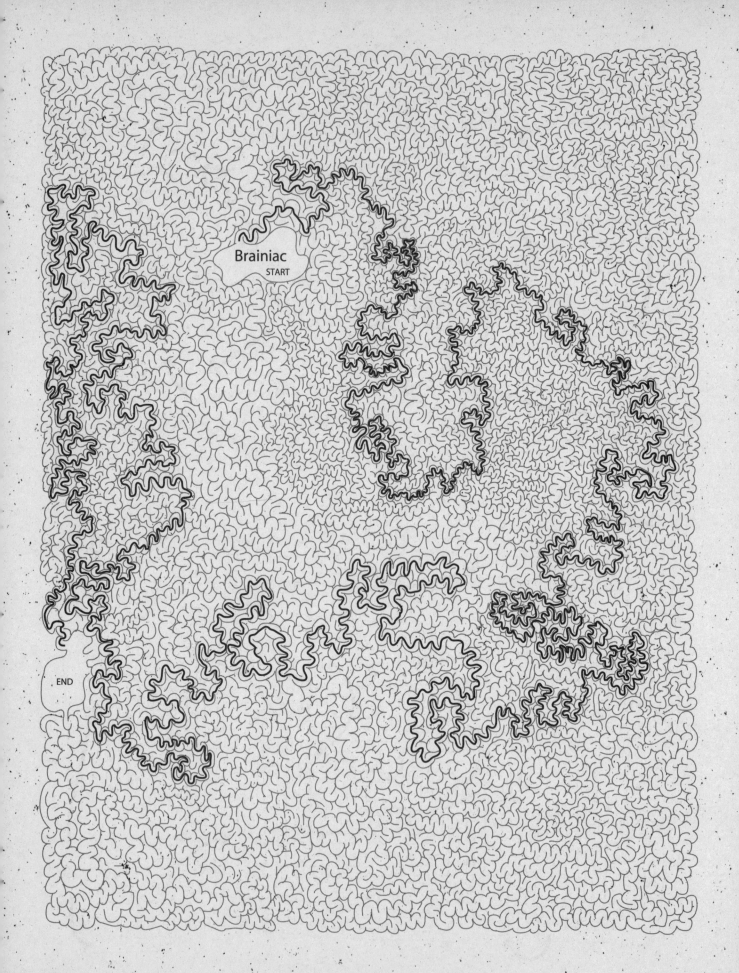

Brainiac

START

END

Solutions • Chapter 6

3-D ILLUSIONS

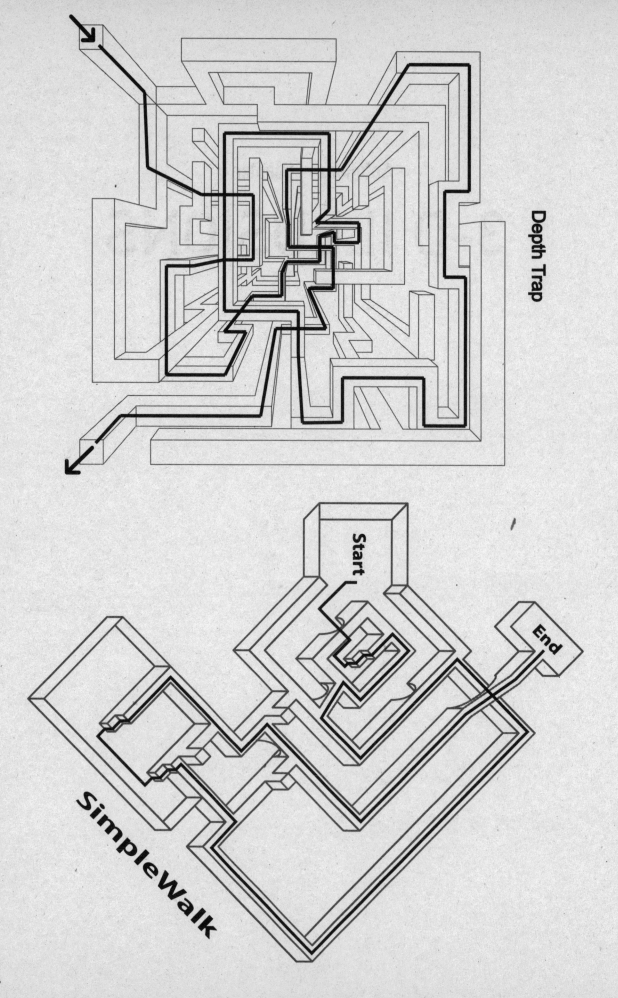

Depth Trap

Start

End

SimpleWalk

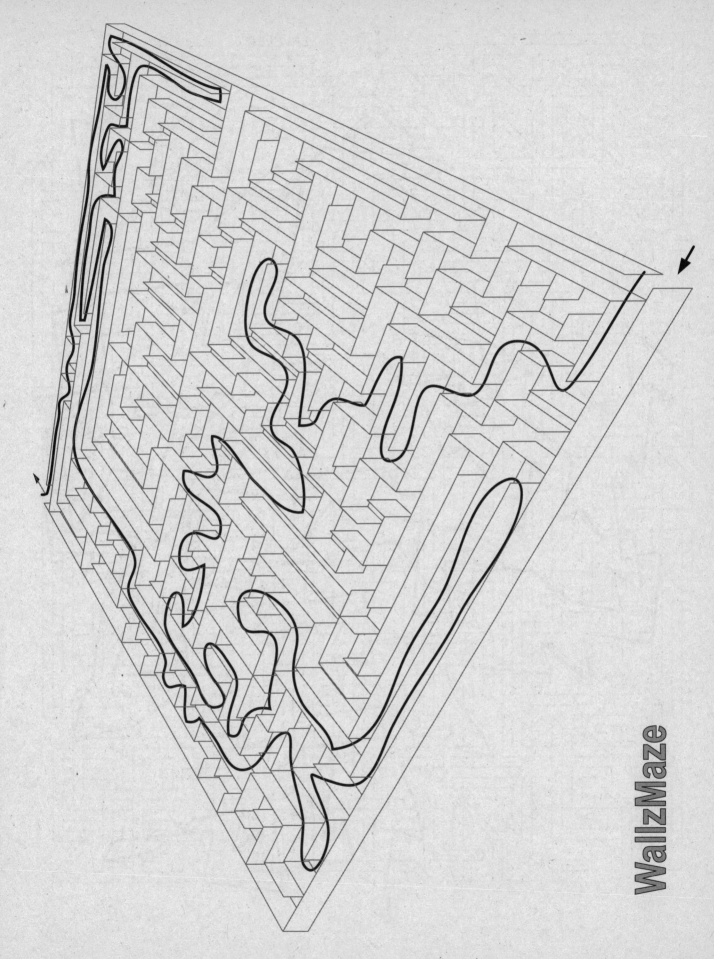

WallzMaze

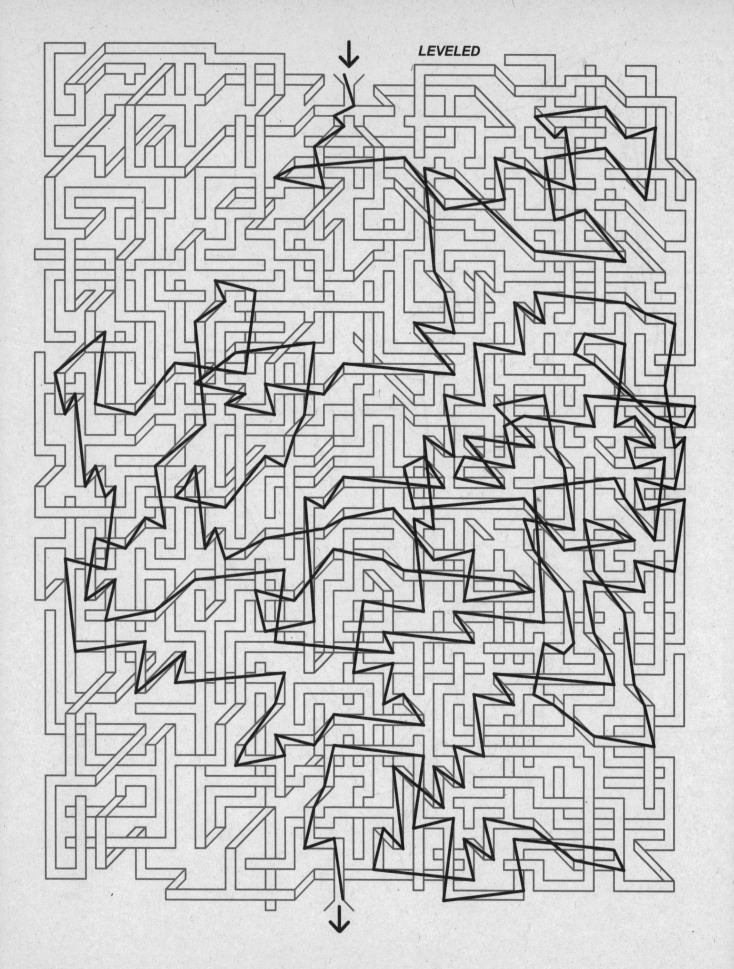

LEVELED

VERTI-WALL

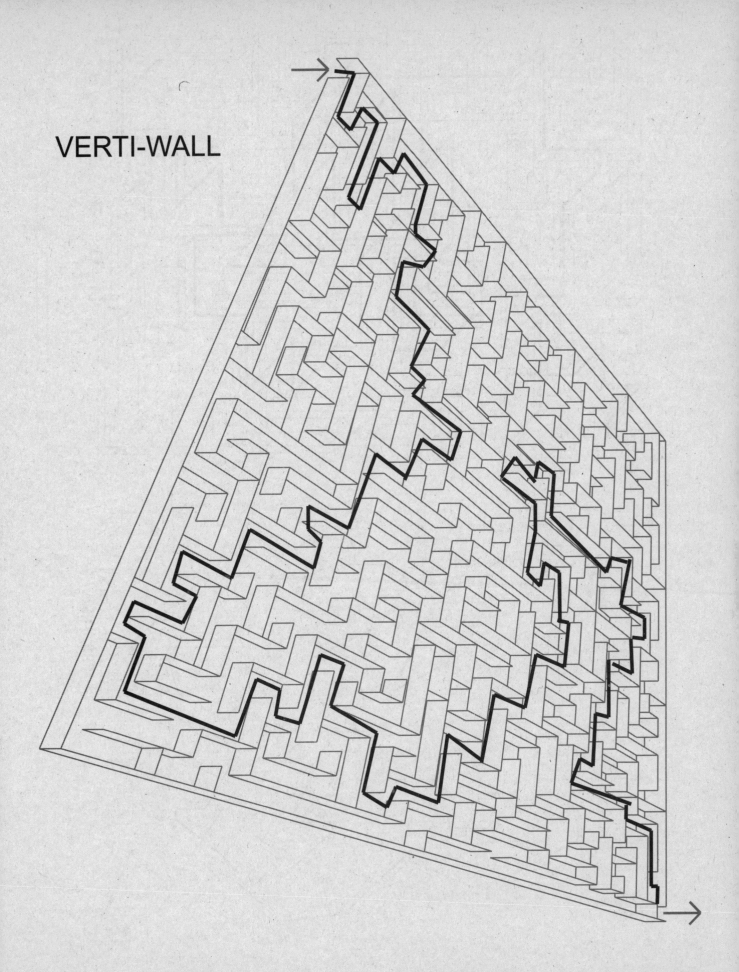

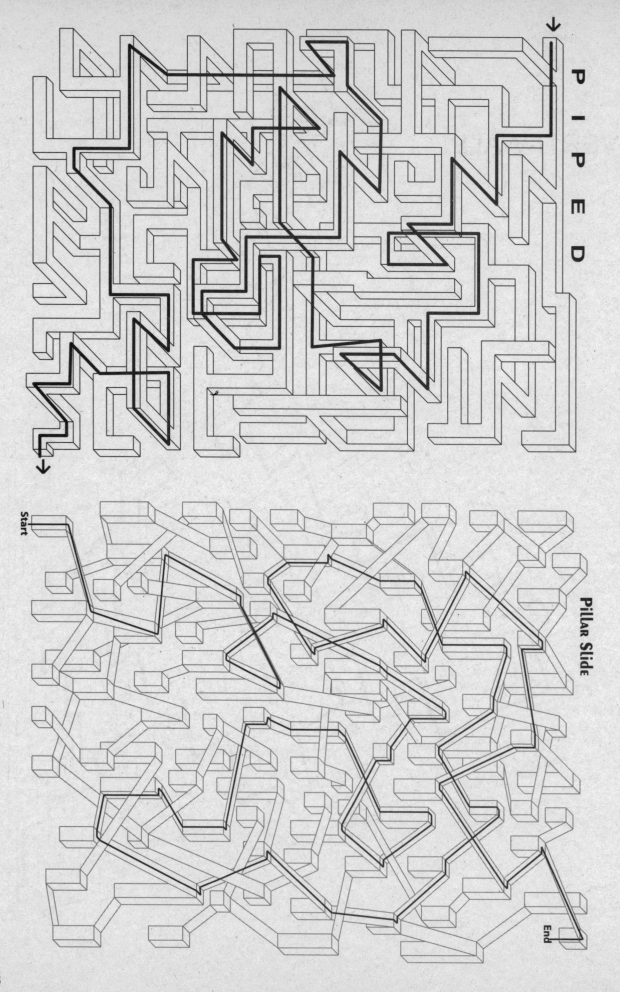

PIPED

Pillar Slide

Start

End

MEGAMAZE
MISCELLANY

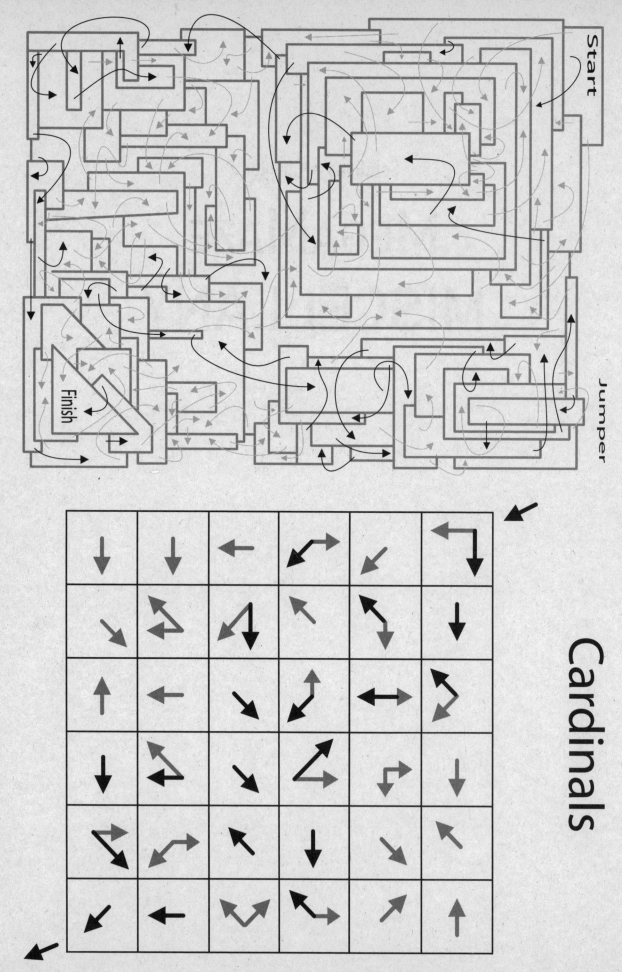

Start

Jumper

Finish

Cardinals

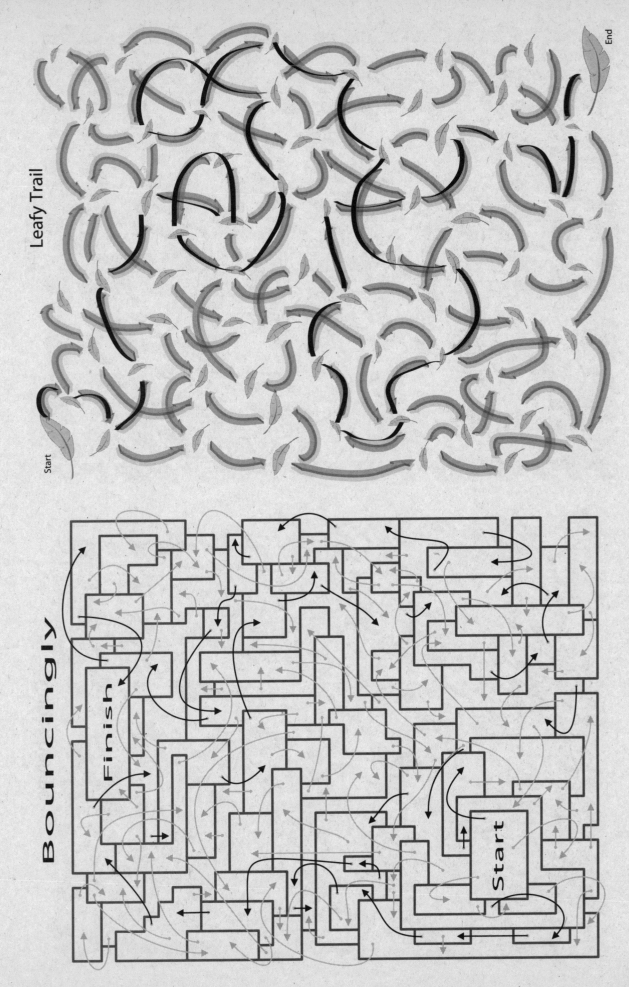

Leafy Trail

Start

End

Bouncingly

Finish

Start

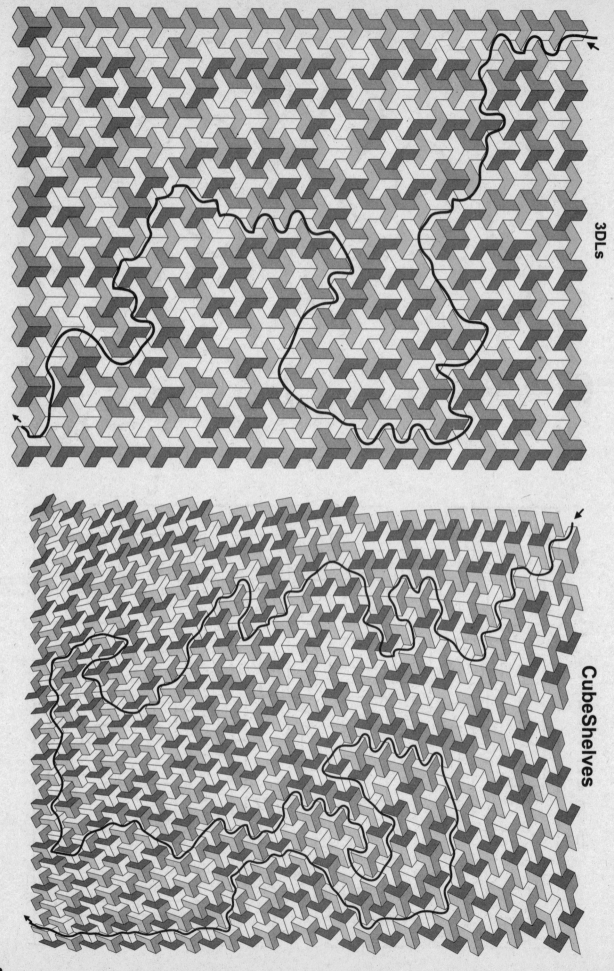

3DLs

CubeShelves

202

Cubezoid Duplicity

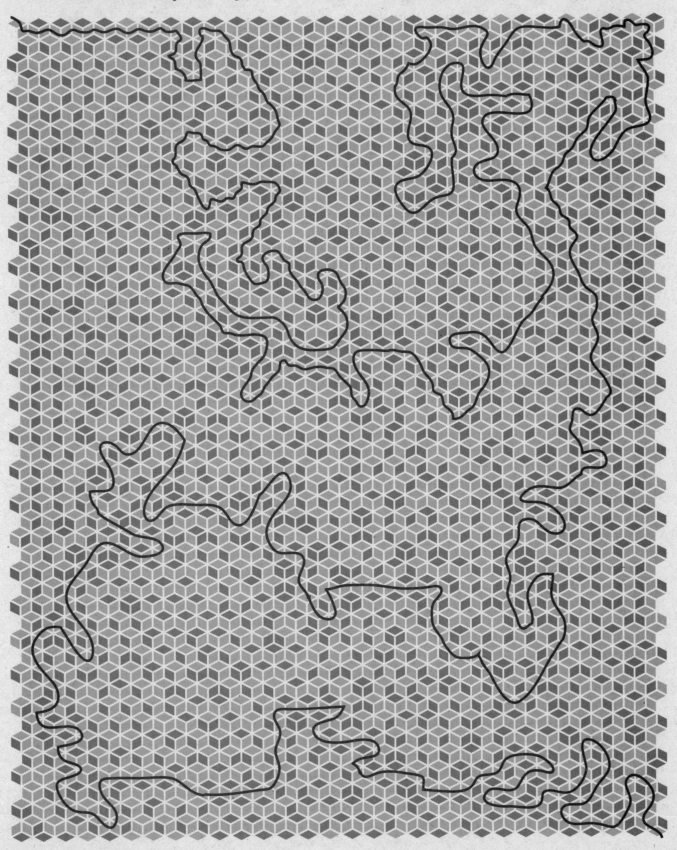

3DLs II

Electroid

START

END

Ice Trail

SHOCKED

Start

End

Start

Finish

MODIFICATIONS

ALTERED STATES

start

finish

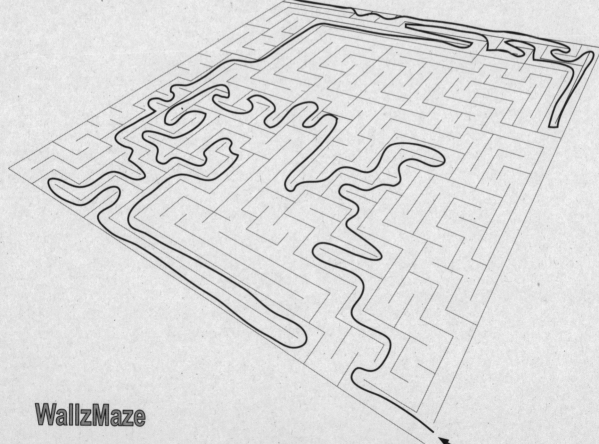

WallzMaze

Start

Finish

Circuitry

HexWare

Gridlocked

Start

Finish

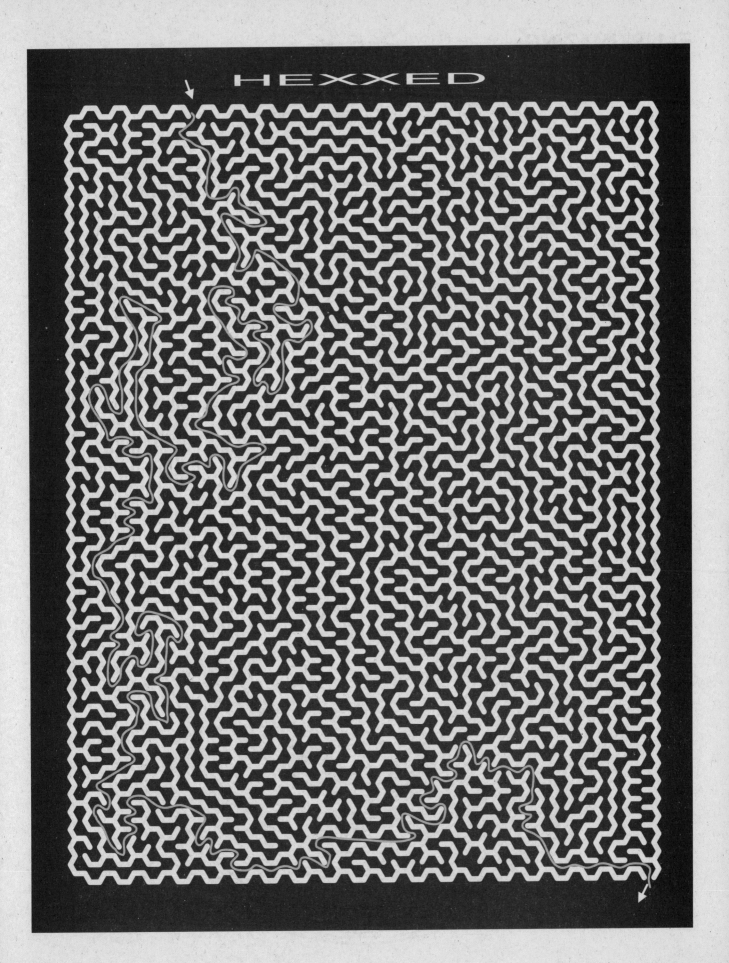

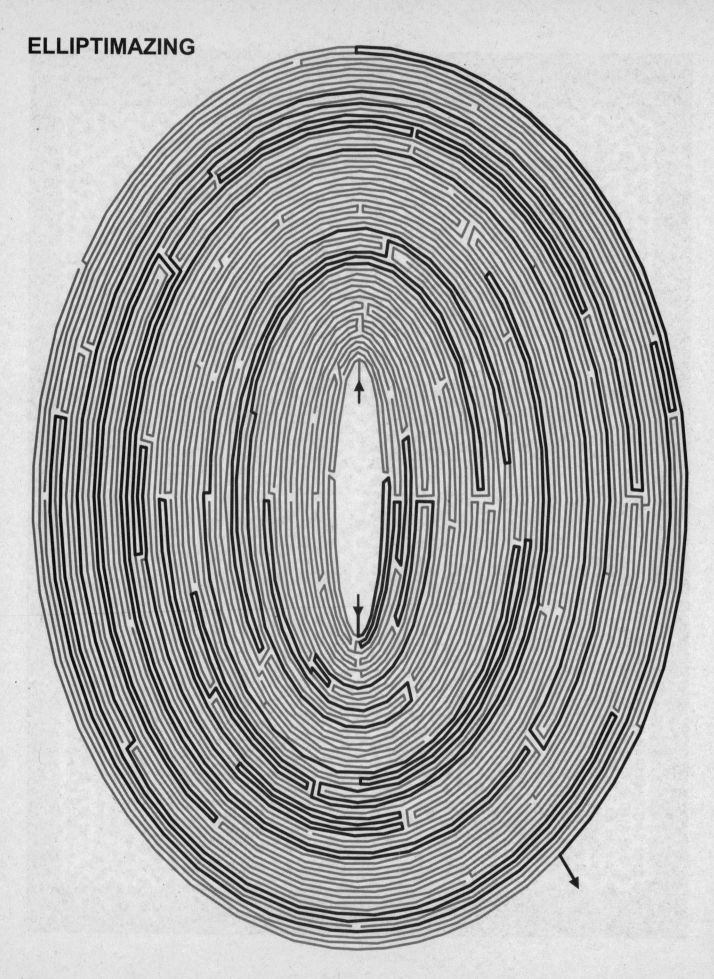

wormlinez

ShutterWarpLines

WarpDrains

Elliptoroid LineMaze

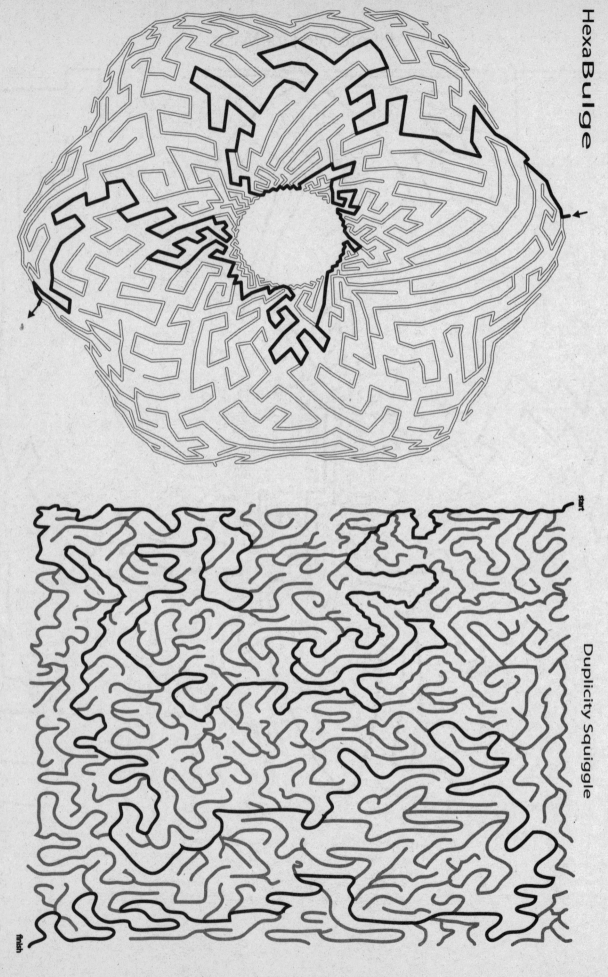

Duplicity Squiggle

start

finish

Electric Flower

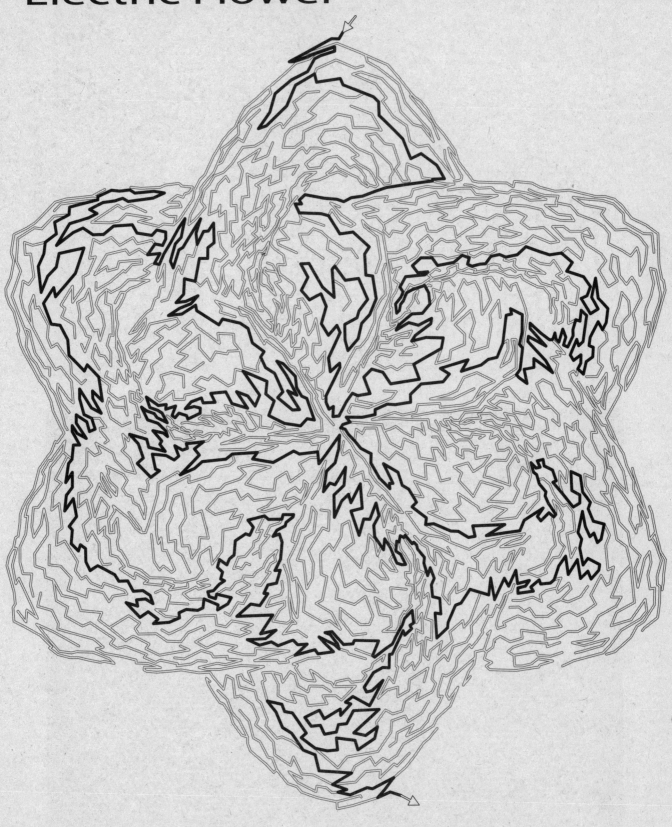

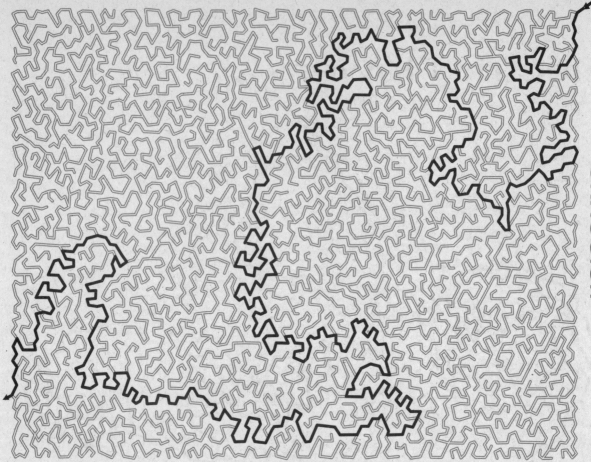

CRAGGISH

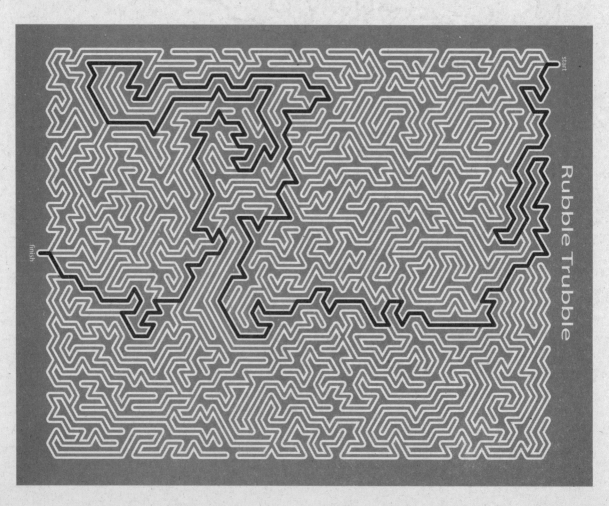

Rubble Trubble

start

finish

Spaghetti Bulge

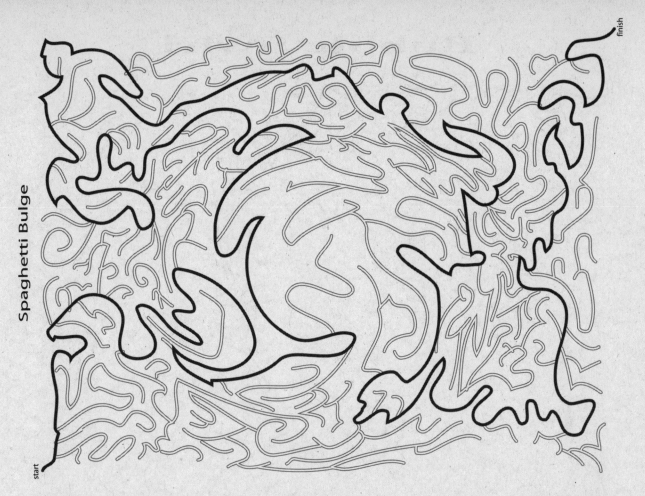

start

finish

Woven Extrusion

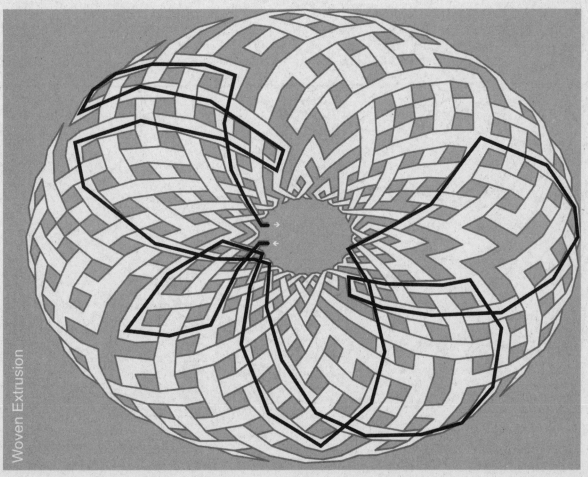

Bubble Swirl

start

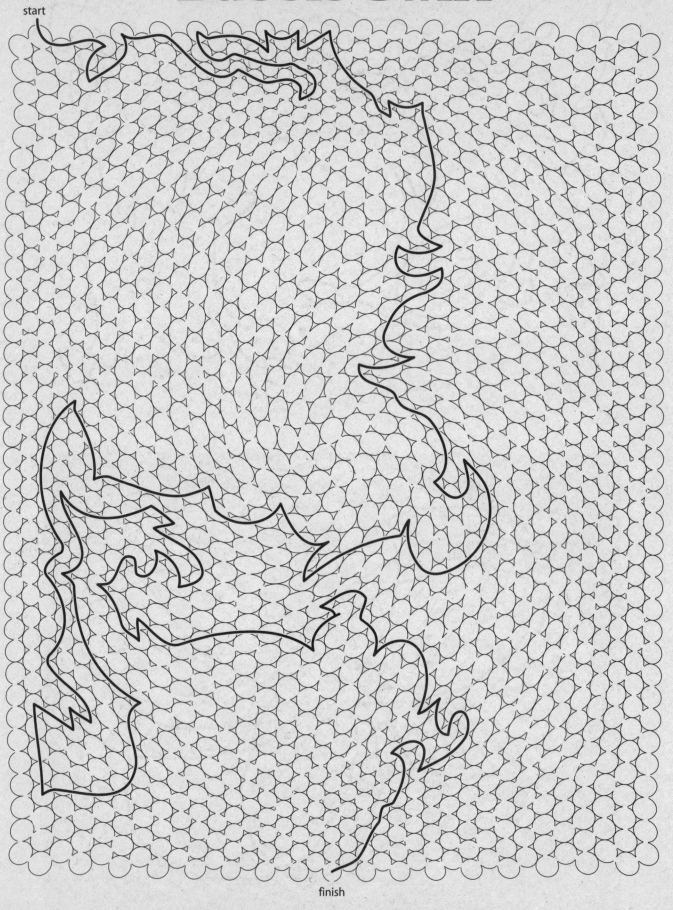

finish

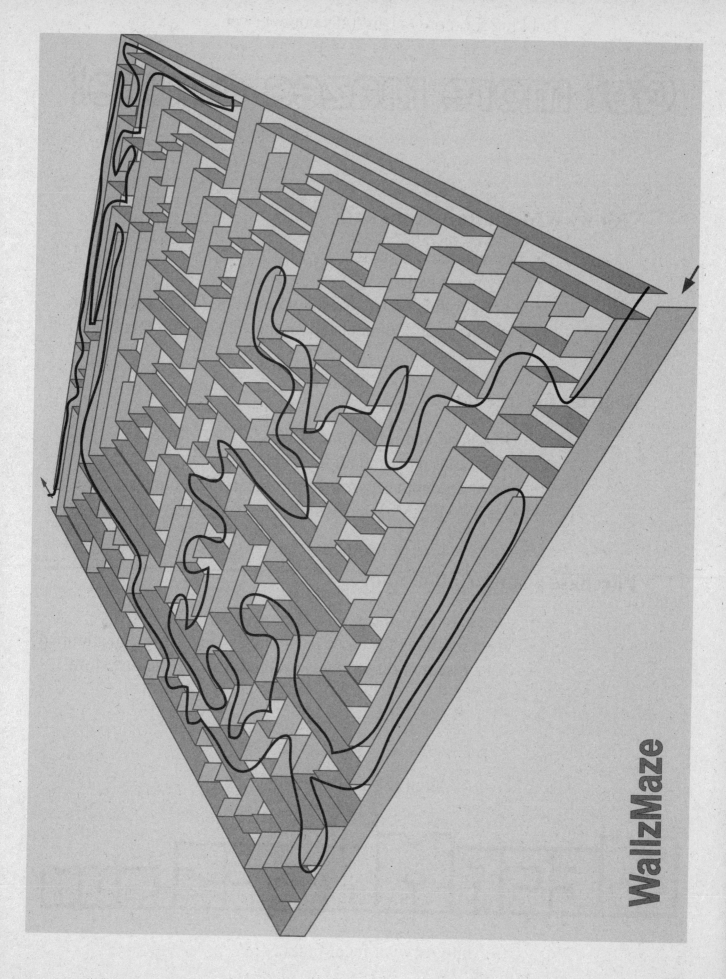

WallzMaze

Looking for more mazes? It's not over yet...

Get more mazes online!

Visit www.MegaMazes.com and:

- See where it all started
- Play maze games
- Let your kids surf a website with clean, old-fashioned fun
- Send us your comments about the website and this book

Register for free to:

- Download and print more mazes
- View color mazes in all their splendor
- See an in-depth preview of the subscriber content
- Get the MegaMazes newsletter

Purchase a subscription and:

- Access to new mazes added every week
- View solutions for those tricky mazes that have you stumped
- Get a discount on products ordered from our online store

All of this and more at:

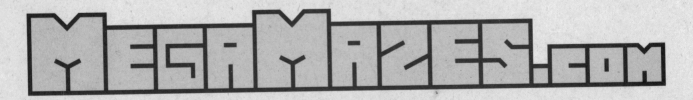

http://www.MegaMazes.com/